EXCURSIONS IN M

❖

NUMBER (

The Backbone of Pascal's Triangle

Martin Griffiths

The United Kingdom Mathematics Trust

The Backbone of Pascal's Triangle

Published by The United Kingdom Mathematics Trust.

Maths Challenges Office, School of Mathematics, University of Leeds, Leeds, LS2 9JT, United Kingdom

http://www.ukmt.org.uk

First published 2008.

ISBN 978-1-906001-04-9

Printed in the UK for the UKMT by Cromwell Press, Trowbridge, Wiltshire.

Typographic design by Andrew Jobbings of Arbelos.

http://www.arbelos.co.uk

Typeset with LATEX.

The books published by the United Kingdom Mathematics Trust are grouped into series.

The EXCURSIONS IN MATHEMATICS series consists of monographs which focus on a particular topic of interest and investigate it in some detail, using a wide range of ideas and techniques. They are aimed at high school students, undergraduates and others who are prepared to pursue a subject in some depth, but do not require specialised knowledge.

1. *The Backbone of Pascal's Triangle*, Martin Griffiths

The HANDBOOKS series is aimed particularly at students at secondary school who are interested in acquiring the knowledge and skills which are useful for tackling challenging problems, such as those posed in the competitions administered by the UKMT and similar organisations.

1. *Plane Euclidean Geometry: Theory and Problems*, A D Gardiner and C J Bradley

2. *Introductions to Number Theory and Inequalities*, C J Bradley

3. *A Mathematical Olympiad Primer*, Geoff C Smith

The PROBLEMS series consists of collections of high-quality and original problems of Olympiad standard.

1. *New Problems in Euclidean Geometry*, David Monk

The YEARBOOKS series documents all the UKMT activities, including details of all the challenge papers and solutions, lists of high scorers, accounts of the IMO and Olympiad training camps, and other information about the Trust's work during each year.

Contents

Series Editor's Foreword

This book is part of a series whose aim is to provide young mathematicians with a chance to engage with a topic in mathematics which is of particular interest to the author. The subject is explored both at length and in depth. At length: the ideas are followed along various paths to see how far they will go and to reveal connections between different parts of mathematics. In depth: the mathematical argument is treated rigorously and difficult steps are carefully explained in a way which is accessible to sixth-form students.

Another feature of the series is that much of the work is left to the reader in the form of exercises, challenges, tasks and research activities. This emphasizes the fact that reading mathematics is an active rather than a passive experience. The satisfaction in understanding challenging ideas is proportional to the effort made in doing so.

I hope that every secondary school will have these books in its library. The prices have been set so low that many good students will wish to purchase their own copies. Schools wishing to give out large numbers of copies of these books as prizes should note that discounts may be negotiated with the UKMT office.

London, UK   GERRY LEVERSHA

About the Author

Before becoming a teacher, Martin Griffiths had a career in the Army, and it was during his PGCE at Nottingham that Martin was hooked by mathematics in the university library. As a result, he is largely self-taught. He is head of mathematics at a grammar school in Colchester, and his teaching experience has been the inspiration for many of his articles in The Mathematical Gazette. He is currently learning Russian and wishes he could pick that up even half as easily as he could mathematics!

Preface

Everything covered in this book is connected to the sequence of numbers:

$$2, 6, 20, 70, 252, 924, 3\,432, \dots .$$

Some readers might recognise this list of numbers straight away, while others will not have seen it before. Either way, students and teachers alike may well be astounded at both the variety and the depth of mathematical ideas that it can lead to. I will demonstrate how the properties of the numbers in this sequence result in some beautiful and occasionally surprising mathematics.

Although very much concerned with the learning and exploration of mathematics, this is in no sense a 'textbook'. The aim is to allow the reader, via a common thread, to encounter various aspects of mathematics in a way that I hope will be simultaneously challenging, enlightening, encouraging and maybe even entertaining. Indeed, this common thread is the sequence of numbers given earlier. I also hope to demonstrate that, contrary to popular belief, mathematics is a field offering plenty of scope for creativity, albeit in a slightly different sense from that possessed by artists or poets for example. In addition to meeting many new mathematical ideas, there will be opportunities to see old ones used in novel ways.

I have tried to make this book as self-contained as possible (hence the inclusion of several appendices), although there may still be occasions when some research on the internet or in a textbook is required. The mathematical knowledge which is assumed is not actually that vast. A basic understanding of calculus, exponentials and logarithms, power series and the factorisation of integers will be sufficient. Yet by the end of this book the reader will have been introduced to a number of relatively sophisticated mathematical ideas and gained some insight into more advanced aspects of mathematics associated with number theory, combinatorics (this will be explained in due course), probability, calculus, special functions, series and analysis.

Although phrases such as "Mathematics is not a spectator sport" are rather clichéd, they do make a serious point. Indeed, any practising mathematician knows that mathematics cannot be mastered passively by simply flicking through a book, however inspiring and well-written that book might be. In order to get the most out of this book it is necessary, at various points, to get very much involved in the exploration of the mathematical ideas that are being developed. These learning opportunities take the form of Challenges, Tasks, Research Activities and Exercises. It is worth discussing each of these in turn.

Challenges   as their name would imply, are not in general straightforward problems. While the odd one or two might be relatively easy, it is not to be expected that all of them will be solved immediately. A degree of determination and ingenuity is required in order to tackle most of the Challenges. However, they have been chosen so that anyone attempting them will get something out of them, whether or not a full solution is obtained at this stage. It is not essential that each one is completed before moving on, although it would be a good idea occasionally to return to any unsolved Challenges.

Tasks   tend to be rather routine in comparison with the Challenges. They are, nonetheless, worthwhile as they can help to reveal some of the structure behind the mathematics. I would recommend that all tasks are completed before moving on.

Research Activities   are suggestions that will allow the broadening of mathematical knowledge and the gaining of a deeper understanding of areas of mathematics that are introduced in this book. Use might be made of the internet or of any relevant book discovered in the library.

Exercises   are provided at the end of most chapters in order to allow the reader to gain familiarity with, and an understanding of, the material contained therein. The questions are graded so that each Exercise tends to start with easier problems and finish with harder ones.

It is important, because of the content of this book, to say something about the nature of proof in mathematics. In order to prove a result to the satisfaction of the mathematical community, arguments need to be absolutely watertight. If an apparent mathematical pattern is spotted then it cannot necessarily be assumed that this pattern will continue indefinitely. Figure 0.1 shows a classic example.

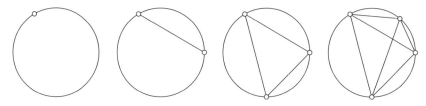

Figure 0.1

This investigation consists of marking n distinct points on the circumference of a circle, drawing chords between every possible pair of points and then counting the number of distinct regions within the circle. The diagrams in Figure 0.1 show the situation for $n = 1, 2, 3, 4$, from which it can be seen that the circles are split up into 1, 2, 4 and 8 regions respectively. What is the maximum possible number of regions for a circle with n points on its circumference? It might be guessed that the answer to this question is 16 when $n = 5$. This does indeed turn out to be correct. What about when $n = 6$? Is the answer 32? It would be easy to assume that this is also correct and that the answer to the more general question is 2^{n-1}. However, a careful check of the situation for $n = 6$ shows that the answer is not 32. In order to obtain the correct formula for the maximum number of regions, the ways that combinations of chords can create these regions need to be considered in detail.

I very much encourage the use of specific examples to illustrate general mathematical ideas. Indeed, many examples shall be employed throughout this book in order to help clarify certain points. However, although specific examples can often give us an idea of how a general proof might proceed, they must not be mistaken for the proof itself. At some points I might say, after a few examples have been considered, that a generalisation follows in an obvious way. If ever anyone feels that this is not totally obvious then they ought to take things a little further and obtain a general proof themselves. The key thing is the appreciation of the need for general proofs in most of the results presented here.

Many mathematicians discover that as their mathematical knowledge expands they become more and more interested in the historical aspect. Indeed, I feel that an awareness of how mathematics has developed over the centuries does allow us more easily to picture this vast body of learning as a whole. I would therefore encourage the reader to find out a little bit more about some of the characters mentioned in this book, and to consider what the state of mathematical knowledge was around the time that they were alive. A good website to visit in this respect is [12].

At this point it is also worth mentioning something about the way that creative mathematics is done in real life, where 'creative mathematics' might include anything from solving a puzzle in a magazine to tackling one of the seven 'Millennium Problems'. It is important to realise that the processes involved in the solutions of difficult problems do not generally correspond to the final polished versions that appear in mathematics books or journals. The very act of extending our knowledge, technique and, most importantly, understanding of mathematics by actually getting stuck in and doing it (through tackling problems, working on projects, undertaking investigations and so on) often takes many twists and turns. From my own experience this process very rarely follows a nice linear progression. To build up the structures, patterns and links in our minds we have to be prepared to veer off at tangents or go down blind alleys, and we should never be afraid of being adventurous in our mathematics.

This book is split into two parts. Although there is certainly some challenging mathematics in Part I, most of this material can be understood by any keen mathematician with a grasp of the topics and techniques mentioned earlier. Part II, on the other hand, contains more demanding material. It is probably best that this is only tackled once the mathematical techniques and ideas introduced in Part I have been mastered. Amongst other things, it is shown in Part II how certain properties of our sequence can be used to obtain information on the way that primes are distributed amongst the positive integers. Even though it might be a little while before some people are ready to take on Part II, there is no harm whatsoever in having an occasional glance through these later chapters in order to see where we are headed. For Chapter 15 in particular, you might find it useful to have a book on elementary number theory to hand. I can certainly recommend [1] as providing an excellent introduction to this area of mathematics.

At various points throughout this book can be seen reference numbers in parenthesis (such as (5.2), for example) next to an equation or expression. These are employed simply for convenience and will allow me to refer to these equations or expressions without having to write them out each time. In order to signify the completion of a proof, a tombstone symbol ❑ is used. It is also worth pointing out, for example, that (5.2) is not to be confused with Result 5.2. The former notation tends to be used to represent intermediate or relatively straightforward results while the latter is generally associated with results for which a full and formal proof is given.

Finally, it is quite possible that some will already be familiar with many or all of the ideas in the introductory chapter. If that is the case then it might be possible to skip sections of this chapter after having had a quick glance through the first few pages in order to ensure familiarity with the notation that will be used throughout the book.

I am very grateful to the editor and to the two anonymous reviewers for the numerous suggestions and insightful comments that they provided throughout the production of this book. The fact that the earlier drafts have seen such an improvement in both clarity and presentation is largely attributable to their efforts.

Colchester, UK   MARTIN GRIFFITHS

Part I

Chapter 1

Introduction

This book is about some of the amazing mathematical ideas and results that can be introduced and developed by looking at a particular sequence of numbers. Let us start by considering a simple scenario that allows us to generate this sequence.

Two teachers, Mr. Hardy and Mrs. Germain, are going to take a class of students on a school trip. Suppose that this class has an even number of students in it so that there are $2n$ students for some positive integer n. Mr. Hardy will be responsible for half the students while Mrs. Germain will look after the remainder. The nth term of our sequence is given by the number of different groups of students that Mrs. Germain could be in charge of.

If there were only 2 students (so that $n = 1$), Alice and Brian, then she could be in charge of the 'group' consisting either of just Alice or just Brian. So the first term of our sequence is 2.

Now say that the class consisted of Alice, Brian, Chris and Deepa (so $n = 2$). Here is a list of the possible groups that Mrs. Germain could be in charge of:

Alice and Brian   Alice and Chris   Alice and Deepa
Brian and Chris   Brian and Deepa   Chris and Deepa

The second term of our sequence is therefore 6.

Task 1.1   Before going any further, list all possible groups of 3 students from Alice, Brian, Chris, Deepa, Edward and Fran. You may find it more convenient to use just their initials. To ensure that you get all possible trios of students it is best to employ some sort of systematic listing procedure. How many different groups did you find?

You should have found that there are 20 such groups. If this is not the case then you will need either to find any missing trios or to search for repeated trios in your list. For greater class sizes this listing process would obviously become very tedious. Is there a more efficient way of enumerating our sequence, preferably via some sort of formula for the nth term?

In our quest for such a formula, let us generalise the situation somewhat and consider the problem of finding out how many different groups of k students it is possible to pick from a class of m students. One important thing to note is that no ordering is implied in these groups of students. So, for example, the group consisting of Alice, Chris and Deepa is to be regarded exactly the same as the group consisting of Alice, Deepa and Chris. A *combination* of k students is an unordered selection whereas a *permutation* of k students is concerned not only with the particular group of k students but also with the order (or arrangement) in which they appear. Thus the two lists of 3 students considered earlier are identical as combinations but distinct as permutations.

A nice example to consider when clarifying the distinction between combinations and permutations is the selection of a cricket team of 11 players from a squad of 15, say. The number of combinations of 11 players from 15 gives the number of possible teams while the number of permutations of 11 from 15 enumerates the number of possible batting orders.

It is clear that we are concerned here with the number of combinations of k students from m rather than the number of permutations. Despite this, however, it turns out that permutations of students do have to be considered in order to obtain our much sought-after general formula.

Imagine all m students in the class standing in a line. Let us take $m = 5$, for example, and consider the following class:

Amir   Betty   Charlie   David   Ellen

How many permutations are possible? In other words, how many different arrangements are there of these students in a line? Well, there are 5 choices for the first person in the line and, once this person has been decided upon, there are 4 remaining possibilities for the second person in the line. Once the second person has been fixed, there are 3 choices for the third person, and so on, as is shown in Figure 1.1. From this it is clear that

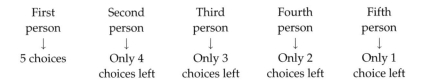

First	Second	Third	Fourth	Fifth
person	person	person	person	person
↓	↓	↓	↓	↓
5 choices	Only 4	Only 3	Only 2	Only 1
	choices left	choices left	choices left	choice left

Figure 1.1

there are $5 \times 4 \times 3 \times 2 \times 1 = 120$ permutations of these students, and that in general there will be $m \times (m-1) \times (m-2) \times \cdots \times 2 \times 1$ permutations.

The expression given above, giving the product of all the integers from 1 to m inclusive, is a bit unwieldy as it stands, and mathematicians use the notation $m!$ to denote this product. We call it 'm factorial' rather than 'm exclamation mark'. For example, $7! = 7 \times 6 \times 5 \times 4 \times 3 \times 2 \times 1 = 5\,040$.

Incidentally, these numbers grow extremely quickly as m increases. I recently posed the following question to a class of twenty seven students, and asked them to make a guess at the answer:

> "Imagine that we wanted a class photograph. The photographer places each of you in one of twenty seven set positions and takes a photograph. She is, however, not happy with the first photograph and so swaps some of you around and takes another one. If she kept doing this until all possible permutations amongst the twenty seven set positions had occurred then how long would it take?"

We first argued about the average length of time between each photograph, and agreed on a minimum of 30 seconds. Students then made guesses, on the basis of this, as to how long the whole procedure would take. Some said several hours while others said all day. One student even joked that it might take a century or so. They were all absolutely staggered when they were told that, ignoring the fact that we would not be around long enough to complete the task, it would take many times longer than the current age of the universe!

Challenge 1.1   Work out approximately how many times longer than the current age of the universe we would need, in theory, in order to take all possible photographs (the age of the universe has been estimated to be somewhere between 13 and 14 billion years).

Getting back to our quest for a formula, one way of selecting k students from m would be to place all of them in a line in random order and then take the first k of them, leaving the remaining $m - k$ students. Let us consider a particular selection (that is, combination) of the first k students. There are $k!$ possible arrangements of these students in the first k positions in the line, and there are also $(m - k)!$ possible arrangements of the remaining $m - k$ students in the last $m - k$ positions in the line, as seen in Figure 1.2. Thus the total number of possible permutations of all

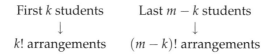

Figure 1.2

the students in the class for which our particular selection of k students occupy the first k positions in the line is $k!(m - k)!$. This would of course be true for any selection of k students from m. In this way we are able to associate each selection of k students from m with precisely $k!(m - k)!$ of the $m!$ possible permutations of the m students in the class. At this point it is important to note the following:

(a) It is not possible, under the above association, for two different selections of k students from m to give rise to the same permutation.

(b) By considering all possible selections of k students from m we obtain, under the above association, all possible permutations for the m students.

In other words, the $m!$ possible permutations of m students can be split into $k!(m - k)!$ equally-sized groups, where each group is associated with a particular selection of k students from m. It must therefore be true that the number of combinations of k from m is given by

$$\frac{m!}{k!(m - k)!}.$$

This result has been arrived at via what is termed a *combinatorial argument* (and *combinatorics* is essentially the branch of mathematics associated with counting mathematical objects). Our combinatorial argument guarantees that the above expression is always an integer, but if we disregard this argument and consider the expression away from our combinatorial context then it is by no means obvious that it will always give us integers. It is actually possible, however, to prove that the above expression is indeed an integer without resorting to a combinatorial argument. One way of doing this is by using a recursive argument based on some results that will be obtained shortly. Another approach utilises simple number-theoretic ideas, and this is the aim of the next Challenge.

Challenge 1.2 Show, by comparing the prime factorisations of the numerator and denominator, that

$$\frac{m!}{k!(m-k)!}$$

is an integer. Note that all you need to do is to show that for any power of a prime appearing in the prime factorisation of the denominator, this prime will appear to at least that power in the prime factorisation of the numerator.

In order to demonstrate the use of the formula given above we now calculate the number of selections of 3 students that are possible from the small class of 5 students mentioned earlier. Note first that, with no restrictions on who goes where, there are $5! = 120$ permutations of this class when they are placed in a line. Also, if a particular trio are restricted to occupying only the first 3 positions then there will be just $3! \times 2! = 12$ permutations possible. For example, with Betty (B), Charlie (C) and Ellen (E) occupying these positions, only the following permutations arise:

BCE AD   BEC AD   CBE AD   CEB AD   EBC AD   ECB AD
BCE DA   BEC DA   CBE DA   CEB DA   EBC DA   ECB DA

There are therefore

$$\frac{5!}{3!(5-3)!} = \frac{5!}{3!2!} = \frac{120}{6 \times 2} = 10$$

selections of 3 students from 5.

The symbol

$$\binom{m}{k}$$

is used to stand for the number of ways of selecting k objects from m distinct objects, and this is termed a *binomial coefficient*. The reason for the words 'binomial' and 'coefficient' will become clear in due course. The symbol ^mC_k is also used for this. Indeed, this will almost certainly be the notation used on your calculator buttons. In order to ensure familiarity with these two notations, we will employ both of them in the following narrative.

Note that

$$\binom{m}{m-k} = \frac{m!}{(m-k)!(m-(m-k))!} = \frac{m!}{(m-k)!k!} = \binom{m}{k} \qquad (1.1)$$

and, after cancelling, we obtain

$$\binom{m}{k} = \frac{m(m-1)(m-2)\ldots(m-k+1)}{k!}. \qquad (1.2)$$

From (1.1) it can be seen that the binomial coefficients possess a symmetry property. This is something that shall be exploited in later chapters. In fact this symmetry can easily be explained from a combinatorial point of view by noting that another way of selecting k objects from m objects is to choose $m - k$ objects, then throw those objects away and select the remaining k objects.

By means of some simple manipulations, a *recurrence relation* for the binomial coefficients can be obtained as follows:

$$\begin{aligned}
\binom{m}{k} + \binom{m}{k+1} &= \frac{m!}{(m-k)!k!} + \frac{m!}{(m-k-1)!(k+1)!} \\
&= \frac{m![(k+1)+(m-k)]}{(m-k)!(k+1)!} \\
&= \frac{(m+1)!}{[(m+1)-(k+1)]!(k+1)!} \\
&= \binom{m+1}{k+1}. \qquad (1.3)
\end{aligned}$$

A recurrence relation expresses later terms in a sequence as a function of earlier ones, thus enabling us eventually to calculate any term in the sequence, even if we do not have an explicit formula for it (noting however, that it is always necessary to know some initial terms in the sequence to allow the recursive process to get started). Probably the most famous recurrence relation is for the *Fibonacci numbers* F_n, given by

$$F_1 = F_2 = 1 \quad \text{and} \quad F_n = F_{n-1} + F_{n-2} \text{ for } n \geq 3.$$

From this the sequence 1, 1, 2, 3, 5, 8, 13, 21, 34, 55, . . . is obtained. Notice how the 'initial conditions' $F_1 = 1$ and $F_2 = 1$ were needed to start the whole recursive process off. Different initial conditions will lead to different sequences.

The recurrence relation (1.3) for the binomial coefficients would appear to be a little more complicated than that for the Fibonacci sequence. This is because (1.3) may be regarded as 'two-dimensional' in the sense that there are two indexing variables, m and k, rather than just the one, as was the case for the Fibonacci recurrence relation. It should be no great surprise, therefore, that it allows us to express the binomial coefficients via a two-dimensional number pattern, commonly referred to as 'Pascal's triangle', the first few rows of which are shown in Table 1.1.

Row																
0								1								
1							1		1							
2						1		2		1						
3					1		3		3		1					
4				1		4		6		4		1				
5			1		5		10		10		5		1			
6		1		6		15		20		15		6		1		
7	1		7		21		35		35		21		7		1	
8	1		8		28		56		70		56		28		8		1

Table 1.1: Pascal's triangle

It can in fact be seen that infinitely many initial conditions are needed to support the recurrence relation (1.3), but luckily they are all relatively trivial and can be summarised as:

$$\binom{m}{0} = 1 \text{ and } \binom{m}{m} = 1 \text{ for } m \geq 0.$$

The first of these is just a statement of the fact that there is only one way of selecting no objects from m objects, and the second says that there is only one way of selecting m objects from m objects. Notice how the initial conditions get the pattern in Pascal's triangle going by supplying all the 1s on the outside. The recurrence relation then allows the pattern on the inside to continue indefinitely since it tells us that the addition of two consecutive entries in any row gives the entry between them in the following row. To be more specific, the sum of the kth and the $(k+1)$th entry from a particular row gives the $(k+1)$th entry in the next row. In fact, ^mC_k is the kth entry in the mth row of Pascal's triangle (on adopting the convention that the uppermost row is the zeroth row and the leftmost entry in any particular row is the zeroth entry of that row). We observe here that the recurrence relation guarantees that the binomial coefficients are always integers.

In the field of mathematics the fact that someone's name is attached to something does not necessarily mean that they were the first person to discover it. Indeed, Pascal's triangle is a case in point. Blaise Pascal was a philosopher and mathematician in 17th century France, and it is certainly true that his detailed analysis of the properties of the binomial coefficients helped lay the foundations of probability theory. Pascal himself called it 'the arithmetical triangle', but after the mathematicians Pierre Rémond de Montmort and Abraham de Moivre referred to it in writing as 'the combinatorial table of Mr. Pascal' (in 1708) and 'Pascal's arithmetical triangle' (in 1730) respectively, the name stuck. However, the Italian mathematician Nicolo Tartaglia actually published these numbers in 1556, over 60 years before Pascal was even born, and there is evidence that the Chinese mathematician Yang Hui was working with these numbers in the 13th century (the Chinese do indeed use the term 'Yang Hui's triangle').

Incidentally, it is also possible to obtain a combinatorial proof of the recurrence relation (1.3). If there are m distinct red objects and 1 blue object then we can choose $k+1$ of these $m+1$ objects in $^{m+1}C_{k+1}$ ways. However, any particular choice of $k+1$ objects will either contain the blue object or it will not. We can thus also enumerate the number of choices of $k+1$ objects from $m+1$ by finding the number of them containing the blue object and the number not containing the blue object and then adding these answers together. Given that the former situation is true there are ^mC_k possible choices (the number of ways of choosing k red objects from the m red objects). On the other hand, if the blue is not amongst our $k+1$ objects then there are $^mC_{k+1}$ choices (the number of ways of choosing $k+1$ red objects from the m red objects). This establishes (1.3) once more.

The *binomial theorem* gives us a way of obtaining, for any non-negative integers k and n with $k \leq n$, the coefficient of x^k in the expansion of $(1+x)^n$. It is called 'binomial' since it involves the expansion of a term involving two numbers. It is possible to visualise $(1+x)^n$ written out as the product of n identical terms $(1+x)(1+x)\ldots(1+x)$, and the expansion that would result on multiplying out the brackets. Each of the 2^n terms in this initial expansion will be the product of r xs and $n-r$ 1s for some non-negative integer r. In order to calculate the coefficient of x^k when this expression is expanded it suffices to know the number of ways that k xs and $n-k$ 1s can be chosen from the n identical terms in the above product. However, we already know that the answer to this is ^nC_k so that

$$(1+x)^n = \sum_{k=0}^{n} \binom{n}{k} x^k. \tag{1.4}$$

The binomial theorem stated above can actually be generalised to cope with expansions of the form $(1+x)^r$ for any real number r. Indeed, this more general theorem is utilised later in the book. See Appendix B for a brief introduction to the generalised binomial theorem and for some associated historical facts.

Challenge 1.3   Pascal's triangle has a three-dimensional analogue called *Pascal's pyramid* which is based on a tetrahedron. See if you can figure out how to construct it. Then relate the numbers in the pyramid to the expansion of $(1+x+y)^n$. Once you have done this you might like to investigate its mathematical properties. Interestingly enough it has an application in the study of genetics.

We are interested here in the special case of the binomial coefficient for which $m = 2n$ and $k = n$, giving us

$$\binom{m}{k} = \binom{2n}{n} = \frac{(2n)!}{n!(2n-n)!} = \frac{(2n)!}{(n!)^2}. \tag{1.5}$$

These are sometimes referred to as the *central binomial coefficients*, for obvious reasons (look down the line of symmetry of Pascal's triangle in Table 1.1). It is worth noting here that some books also define central binomial coefficients for odd m, $m = 2n+1$ say, in which case there are two of them, given by

$$\binom{2n+1}{n} \text{ and } \binom{2n+1}{n+1}, \ n \geq 1.$$

These appear as the identical central pair of entries in the middle of the odd-numbered rows of Pascal's triangle, as can be seen by considering Table 1.1. However, this definition is not adopted here, and from now on it can be assumed that any reference to 'central binomial coefficients' pertains to even m. To take some examples,

$$\binom{2}{1} = \frac{2!}{(1!)^2} = 2, \quad \binom{4}{2} = \frac{4!}{(2!)^2} = 6 \text{ and } \binom{6}{3} = \frac{6!}{(3!)^2} = 20,$$

each of which agree with the results we had obtained earlier by tediously listing the possibilities.

Challenge 1.4   Give a quick proof that $^{2n}C_n$ is, for $n \geq 1$, always even (and so composite for $n \geq 2$). You could use algebra, counting or the properties of Pascal's triangle.

The sequence of central binomial coefficients actually has its own very simple recurrence relation:

$$\begin{aligned}
\binom{2(n+1)}{n+1} &= \frac{[2(n+1)]!}{[(n+1)!]^2} \\
&= \frac{2(n+1) \times (2n+1) \times (2n)!}{(n+1)^2(n!)^2} \\
&= \frac{2(2n+1)}{n+1}\binom{2n}{n}.
\end{aligned} \tag{1.6}$$

This allows us, given one term in the sequence, to calculate the next one in a straightforward manner. For example, if it is known that the fourth term in the sequence is 70 then the next term is

$$\frac{2(2 \times 4 + 1)}{4+1}\binom{8}{4} = \frac{18}{5} \times 70 = 252.$$

Task 1.2   Use the recurrence relation (1.6) along with the fact that $^{10}C_5 = 252$ to calculate $^{12}C_6$ and $^{14}C_7$.

We introduced $^{2n}C_n$ by counting the number of possible selections of n students from $2n$. This can be regarded as a particular way of generating the numbers in this sequence combinatorially, or a *combinatorial interpretation* of $^{2n}C_n$. Our argument to obtain the formula for the nth term effectively boiled down to finding the number of permutations of the $2n$ students in a line and then dividing through by the number of these permutations for which any particular group of n people occupied the first n positions in the line. An alternative, though equivalent, way of enumerating $^{2n}C_n$ would be to line the students up in some fixed arrangement (in alphabetical order, for example) and then give half of them cards with A on, and the other half cards with B on. For example, if $n = 5$ then the issued cards may be in the following order:

BAAABBABAB.

If, without loss of generality, the people holding a card with A on it are designated to be our group of n, then for the above arrangement of n As and n Bs we would choose the second, third, fourth, seventh and ninth students in the line. Each possible arrangement of these letters corresponds to a particular selection of n students from $2n$. On the other hand, with the students in this fixed arrangement, each selection of n people corresponds to the unique arrangement of n As and n Bs in a line for which the positions of the As are determined by the positions of the people in that group. Thus there is what is termed a *one-to-one correspondence* (see Appendix D) between the number of selections of n people from $2n$, and the number of arrangements of n As and n Bs in a line. This tells us that $^{2n}C_n$ is also given by the number of arrangements of n As and n Bs in a line, which can be thought of as an alternative combinatorial interpretation of these numbers. Here, for example, are the 20 possible arrangements for $n = 3$:

AAABBB	AABABB	AABBAB	AABBBA	ABAABB
ABABAB	ABABBA	ABBAAB	ABBABA	ABBBAA
BBBAAA	BBABAA	BBAABA	BBAAAB	BABBAA
BABABA	BABAAB	BAABBA	BAABAB	BAAABB

It quite often happens that the same sequence of numbers arise from what would appear to be different combinatorial situations. In the above example the reason that these different combinatorial situations lead to the same sequence is relatively transparent, and it is easy to establish a one-to-one correspondence between the things being counted. Situations may be encountered, however, for which one-to-one correspondences are far less obvious and require a little more effort to establish (as we shall see in later chapters).

Exercise 1

1. Use (1.2) (and (1.1) when appropriate) to calculate the following. Please resist the temptation to use a calculator!

   (a) $\binom{7}{4}$ (b) $\binom{10}{3}$ (c) $\binom{20}{18}$

2. Calculate the coefficient of x^7 in

   (a) $(1+x)^{14}$ (b) $(1-x)^{14}$ (c) $(2+x)^{14}$.

3. Prove, both algebraically and by using a combinatorial argument, that
   $$m\binom{n}{m} = n\binom{n-1}{m-1}.$$

4. By using the binomial theorem, or otherwise, show that for $n \geq 1$:

   (a) $\binom{n}{0} + 2\binom{n}{1} + 2^2\binom{n}{2} + \cdots + 2^n\binom{n}{n} = 3^n$

   (b) $\binom{n}{0} - \binom{n}{1} + \binom{n}{2} - \cdots + (-1)^n\binom{n}{n} = 0$

   (c) $\binom{n}{1} + 2\binom{n}{2} + 3\binom{n}{3} + \cdots + n\binom{n}{n} = n \times 2^{n-1}$.

5. (a) Verify that each of the following are true:

   (i) $\binom{7}{3}\binom{3}{2} = \binom{7}{2}\binom{5}{1}$

   (ii) $\binom{12}{9}\binom{9}{5} = \binom{12}{5}\binom{7}{4}$.

   (b) Find, with proof, a generalisation of the results in part (a).

6. Prove the following connection between binomial coefficients and Fibonacci numbers, for $n \geq 0$:
   $$F_{2n+1} = \binom{2n}{0} + \binom{2n-1}{1} + \binom{2n-2}{2} + \cdots + \binom{n}{n}.$$

Chapter 2

Some mathematical properties of $^{2n}C_n$

The real theme of this book is the mathematics associated with, and arising from, the particular (central) binomial coefficients $^{2n}C_n$. There is an incredible variety and richness of mathematical ideas connected to these numbers. In this chapter we give some interesting results concerning the central binomial coefficients that will be used at various places throughout this book. Note that $^{2n}C_n$ stands for the nth central binomial coefficient while $\{^{2n}C_n\}$ denotes the complete sequence of these numbers.

Table 2.1 gives the values of $^{2n}C_n$ for the first few values of n (see Appendix E for a more comprehensive list):

n	1	2	3	4	5	6	7	8
$^{2n}C_n$	2	6	20	70	252	924	3 432	12 870

Table 2.1: Values of $^{2n}C_n$

It seems that these numbers are increasing in an exponential fashion, and you might even have gone as far as to conjecture that the ratio between successive terms in the sequence approaches 4. This is actually the case, as the next result shows.

Result 2.1

$$\frac{^{2(n+1)}C_{n+1}}{^{2n}C_n} \to 4 \text{ as } n \to \infty.$$

PROOF The recurrence relation (1.6) gives

$$\frac{^{2(n+1)}C_{n+1}}{^{2n}C_n} = \frac{2(2n+1)}{n+1} = \frac{4(n+1)-2}{n+1} = 4 - \frac{2}{n+1} \rightarrow 4 \text{ as } n \rightarrow \infty.$$

❑

In this chapter we will also obtain several slightly deeper results giving some of the fundamental mathematical properties of $^{2n}C_n$, most of which will be utilised in later chapters.

Before we give the next result concerning $^{2n}C_n$, consider the following simple and well-known result concerning a sum of binomial coefficients, obtained by putting $x = 1$ in the binomial theorem (1.4) to give:

$$2^n = (1+1)^n = \sum_{k=0}^{n} 1^k \binom{n}{k} = \sum_{k=0}^{n} \binom{n}{k}.$$

It turns out that there is actually a slightly more interesting way to obtain this result. Imagine n distinct objects laid out on a table. By way of a specific example suppose that there are four individual pieces of fruit:

Banana   Apple   Orange   Pear

Let us count the number of possible subsets of this set of four pieces of fruit, including the *empty set* consisting of no fruit at all. It is of course possible to go through the tedious process of listing all of these subsets, as follows:

(1) Empty set	(5) P	(9) A and O	(13) B, A and P
(2) B	(6) B and A	(10) A and P	(14) B, O and P
(3) A	(7) B and O	(11) O and P	(15) A, O and P
(4) O	(8) B and P	(12) B, A and O	(16) B, A, O and P

However, there are cleverer ways to perform this enumeration. First, each of the subsets above can be matched with a four-digit binary number. Consider, for example, the subset given in (14) above. With a 1 indicating that a fruit is in the subset and a 0 denoting otherwise then, maintaining the order BAOP given in the original list of fruit, it can be seen that the subset in (14) corresponds to 1011. In fact it is clear that every four-digit binary number corresponds to a particular subset and that different numbers lead to different subsets. Likewise, every subset corresponds to a particular four-digit binary number, with different subsets leading to different numbers, thereby establishing another one-to-one correspondence (see Appendix D). From this it follows that the number of subsets is equal to the number of four-digit binary numbers, which is 2^4.

Secondly, note that ^4C_k gives the number of subsets of size k, so that the total number of subsets of the four pieces of fruit is

$$\binom{4}{0} + \binom{4}{1} + \binom{4}{2} + \binom{4}{3} + \binom{4}{4}.$$

From this it follows that

$$\sum_{k=0}^{4} \binom{4}{k} = 2^4,$$

a result which generalises in an obvious way to sets of size n. This example illustrates quite nicely a common procedure in combinatorics whereby an identity is established by counting the same thing in two different ways.

Interestingly enough, if, instead of the sum of the binomial coefficients given above, we consider the sum of their squares then the following result emerges:

Result 2.2

$$\sum_{k=0}^{n} \binom{n}{k}^2 = \binom{2n}{n}.$$

PROOF Suppose that a team of n students is to be chosen from a class of $2n$ students. The right-hand side gives the number of possible teams. Say that the class has equal numbers of boys and girls (that is, n of each). Then the team could consist of 0 boys and n girls, or 1 boy and $n-1$ girls, and so on, as shown below:

Number of boys	0	1	2	...	$n-1$	n
Number of girls	n	$n-1$	$n-2$	...	1	0

The number of ways of choosing k boys and $n-k$ girls is

$$\binom{n}{k} \times \binom{n}{n-k} = \binom{n}{k}^2,$$

on using (1.1). Thus summing this expression from $k = 0$ to $k = n$ also gives us the number of ways of choosing a team of n from $2n$, as required. ❑

Result 2.2 was obtained by using a combinatorial argument, but it can also be proved algebraically. Indeed, an algebraic proof of this result appears in Chapter 9. It is not difficult, and you might want to look at it before moving on with the rest of this chapter.

Result 2.3

$$\sum_{k=n-1}^{2n-1} \binom{k}{n-1} = \binom{2n}{n}.$$

PROOF Consider first the term $^{2n-1}C_{n-1}$ in the sum on the left. If we imagine $2n$ people standing in a line then this term represents, for example, the number of selections of $n-1$ people from the first $2n-1$ in this line. If with each of these selections is included the person standing at position $2n$ then all possible selections of n from $2n$ such that the last person chosen is at position $2n$ will have been accounted for.

Next, the term $^{2n-2}C_{n-1}$ enumerates all possible selections of $n-1$ people from the first $2n-2$ in the line. If we now include, with each of these selections, the person at position $2n-1$ then all possible selections of n from $2n$ such that the last person chosen is at position $2n-1$ will have been obtained. The key thing to note here is that none of these selections coincide exactly with any of those made in the first paragraph since the last person in the selection cannot simultaneously be in position $2n-1$ and position $2n$.

It is clearly possible to continue in this manner with $^{2n-k}C_{n-1}$ enumerating the selections of n from $2n$ such the last person is at position $2n-k+1$, for $1 \le k \le n+1$. This covers all possible selections of n people from the $2n$ in our line, and our combinatorial proof of the identity is thus complete.

The above can be summarised by the diagrams in Figure 2.1 on the facing page, where S represents a person that has been selected and N represents one that has not.   ❏

In order to introduce the next result let us imagine tossing a fair coin $2n$ times. What is the most likely number of heads to appear? There are 2^{2n} possible outcomes when a coin is tossed $2n$ times, $^{2n}C_k$ of which contain exactly k heads. So the probability that exactly k heads appear among the $2n$ tosses is $^{2n}C_k \div 2^{2n}$ and, in order to answer our question, we just need to find the value of k that maximises $^{2n}C_k$. Result 2.4 tells us that that the most likely outcome is an equal number of heads and tails.

First $2n - 1$ people	S	
$n - 1$ selected	$2n$th person	

First $2n - 2$ people	S	N
$n - 1$ selected	$(2n - 1)$th person	1 person

First $2n - 3$ people	S	NN
$n - 1$ selected	$(2n - 2)$th person	2 people

$\vdots$ $\qquad$ $\vdots$ $\qquad$ $\vdots$

First $n - 1$ people	S	NNN...NN
$n - 1$ selected	nth person	n people

Figure 2.1

Result 2.4 *The central binomial coefficient is the largest out of all numbers of the form $^{2n}C_k$ with $0 \le k \le 2n$.*

PROOF Note that

$$\frac{^{2n}C_{k+1}}{^{2n}C_k} = \frac{k!(2n - k)!(2n)!}{(k+1)!(2n - k - 1)!(2n)!} = \frac{2n - k}{k + 1},$$

so for $0 \le k \le 2n - 1$ it is true that $^{2n}C_{k+1} > {}^{2n}C_k$ if, and only if, $2n - k > k + 1$. In other words, when $0 \le k \le 2n - 1$ then $^{2n}C_{k+1} > {}^{2n}C_k$ if, and only if, $k \le n - 1$.

From this it is clear that $^{2n}C_n$ is the largest number of the form $^{2n}C_k$, for $0 \le k \le 2n$, as required. ❏

On looking along any row of Pascal's triangle in Table 1.1 on page 9 it can be seen that the entries increase in size until the middle of the row has been reached and then decrease in size to the end of the row. The observations made in proving Result 2.4 provide an algebraic confirmation of this property of Pascal's triangle for the even-numbered rows (and a similar argument will show that this is also true for the odd-numbered rows).

We now obtain some bounds on the size of $^{2n}C_n$ in terms of simple functions:

Result 2.5

$$\frac{2^{2n-1}}{n} < \binom{2n}{n} < 2^{2n} \text{ for } n \ge 2.$$

PROOF The upper bound is immediate on using the binomial theorem:

$$2^{2n} = (1+1)^{2n}$$

$$= \binom{2n}{0} + \binom{2n}{1} + \cdots + \binom{2n}{n} + \cdots + \binom{2n}{2n}$$

$$> \binom{2n}{n} \text{ for } n \geq 1.$$

To obtain the lower bound it may be noted that if $n \geq 2$ then

$$\binom{2n}{0} + \binom{2n}{2n} = 2 < \binom{2n}{n}$$

and, from Result 2.4,

$$\binom{2n}{k} \leq \binom{2n}{n} \text{ for } 1 \leq k \leq 2n - 1.$$

Therefore

$$2^{2n} = \binom{2n}{0} + \binom{2n}{1} + \binom{2n}{2} + \cdots + \binom{2n}{2n-1} + \binom{2n}{2n}$$

$$= \left[\binom{2n}{0} + \binom{2n}{2n}\right] + \binom{2n}{1} + \binom{2n}{2} + \cdots + \binom{2n}{2n-1}$$

$$< 2n \binom{2n}{n},$$

which gives the lower bound. ❏

The upper and lower bounds for $^{2n}C_n$ obtained in Result 2.5 will prove useful later, together with more accurate estimates derived by more intricate arguments in Chapter 5.

The next result concerns the possible prime factors of $^{2n}C_n$. As will be shown, it is actually quite easy to obtain some general information regarding the appearance or non-appearance of certain primes in the prime factorisation of $^{2n}C_n$.

Result 2.6 *For any prime number p:*

(a) *if $n + 1 \leq p \leq 2n$ then p is a factor of $^{2n}C_n$;*

(b) *if $\frac{2n}{3} < p \leq n$ then p is not a factor of $^{2n}C_n$ when $n \geq 3$.*

PROOF The result given in part (a) is clear since all primes such that $n+1 \le p \le 2n$ will appear in the numerator of

$$\binom{2n}{n} = \frac{2n \times (2n-1) \times (2n-2) \times \cdots \times (n+2) \times (n+1)}{n \times (n-1) \times (n-2) \times \cdots \times 2 \times 1}$$

but none of them can be cancelled by any of the terms in the denominator since 1 is the only positive integer less than p that divides p. For example,

$$\binom{10}{5} = \frac{10 \times 9 \times 8 \times 7 \times 6}{5 \times 4 \times 3 \times 2 \times 1} = 252 = 2^2 \times 3^2 \times 7.$$

Note, however, that if a prime is a factor of the numerator then it will not necessarily be a factor of $^{2n}C_n$. The above example shows that although 5 is a factor of the numerator, it does not appear in the prime factorisation of $^{10}C_5$.

At this point we define some notation. The symbol $\mid$ denotes 'divides' and $\prod$ is used to define a product of terms in much the same way that Σ is used to define a sum of terms. So, for example, the statements $6|24$ and $a|b$ mean '6 is factor of 24' and 'a is a factor of b' respectively, while

$$\prod_{k=1}^{3} k^2 = 1^2 \times 2^2 \times 3^2 = 36.$$

Using (a) it is clear that

$$\prod_{n<p\le 2n} p \ \Big| \ \binom{2n}{n}. \tag{2.1}$$

In order to demonstrate the truth of (b) let us assume that $\frac{2n}{3} < p \le n$ and $n \ge 3$. With this restriction on p it follows that $2p \le 2n < 3p$, so both p and $2p$ appear as terms in the product for $(2n)!$ but $3p$ does not. Thus, since $\frac{2n}{3} < p \le n$ and $n \ge 3$ imply that p is an odd prime, p^2 divides $(2n)!$ while p^3 does not. Also, p appears as a term in the product for $n!$ but $2p$ does not, so that p divides $n!$ while p^2 does not. Therefore p appears exactly once (that is, to the power 1) in the prime factorisation of $n!$ and exactly twice (that is, to the power 2) in the prime factorisation of $(2n)!$. Thus, before cancelling, both the numerator and the denominator of $^{2n}C_n$ will have p^2 as a term in their prime factorisations. As a consequence, p does not appear in the prime factorisation of $^{2n}C_n$. To take an example, let

$n = 7$ and $p = 5$, noting that $\frac{2n}{3} < p \le n$ in this case. Then

$$\binom{2n}{n} = \binom{14}{7}$$
$$= \frac{14 \times 13 \times 12 \times 11 \times 10 \times 9 \times 8 \times 7 \times 6 \times 5 \times 4 \times 3 \times 2 \times 1}{(7 \times 6 \times 5 \times 4 \times 3 \times 2 \times 1)^2},$$

from which it can be seen that the 5 appears twice in the denominator and twice in the numerator (one of which occurs as a factor of the 10).   ❏

The results obtained above concerning the prime factorisation of $^{2n}C_n$ may seem a little esoteric, but we shall utilise them to great effect later on in order to prove some quite deep results about the distribution of the prime numbers.

Task 2.1   In the proof of Result 2.6 (a) we obtained (2.1):

$$\prod_{n < p \le 2n} p \ \Bigg|\ \binom{2n}{n}.$$

Demonstrate the truth of this last result for the special case $n = 7$.

Challenge 2.1   Show that if p is a prime such that $\frac{n}{2} < p \le \frac{2n}{3}$ then p does appear in the prime factorisation of $^{2n}C_n$ when $n \ge 5$.

Exercise 2

1. Use Result 2.6 to state five primes that will definitely divide $^{46}C_{23}$ and three primes that definitely will not.

2. Using Result 2.6, show that $^{76}C_{38}$ is not divisible by $^{50}C_{25}$.

3. **Devise a combinatorial argument to prove that**

$$\sum_{k=0}^{n} \binom{n+k-1}{k} = \binom{2n}{n} \text{ for } n \geq 1.$$

4. **Show that**

$$\binom{2n}{n} = 2^{2n} \times \frac{1 \times 3 \times 5 \times \cdots \times (2n-1)}{2 \times 4 \times 6 \times \cdots \times 2n}.$$

5. **Adapt the proof of Result 2.5 to show that**

$$\frac{2^{2n+1}}{2n+1} < \binom{2n+1}{n} < 2^{2n} \text{ for } n \geq 1.$$

6. **Use a combinatorial argument to show that**

$$\sum_{k=0}^{n-1} \binom{n-1}{k}\binom{n+1}{k+1} = \binom{2n}{n} \text{ for } n \geq 1.$$

Chapter 3

Other combinatorial interpretations of $^{2n}C_n$

Although this interpretation might not be obvious initially, $^{2n}C_n$ also gives the number of ways of partitioning n as an ordered sum of $n + 1$ non-negative integers. Here, for example, are all the possible outcomes for $n = 3$:

$3+0+0+0$	$0+3+0+0$	$0+0+3+0$	$0+0+0+3$
$2+1+0+0$	$2+0+1+0$	$2+0+0+1$	$1+2+0+0$
$0+2+1+0$	$0+2+0+1$	$1+0+2+0$	$0+1+2+0$
$0+0+2+1$	$1+0+0+2$	$0+1+0+2$	$0+0+1+2$
$1+1+1+0$	$1+1+0+1$	$1+0+1+1$	$0+1+1+1$

Table 3.1: Partitions of 3

There are 20 outcomes for $n = 3$, which does correspond to $^6C_3$.

Task 3.1   List all the partitions of 2 as an ordered sum of 3 non-negative integers to confirm that there are indeed $^4C_2$ outcomes.

To prove the above claim, consider the following method for generating partitions of the integer m as an ordered sum of $k \leq m$ *positive* integers. First write out a series of m 1s and then choose $k - 1$ of the $m - 1$ spaces between them. For example, if $m = 7$ and $k = 3$ then we set out seven 1s in a line and choose two of the six spaces between them as indicated by the arrows:

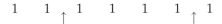

This corresponds to the partition $2 + 4 + 1$ of 7 as an ordered sum of three positive integers. Notice that the two spaces from six can be chosen in $^6C_2 = 15$ ways, so there are 15 partitions of 7 as an ordered sum of three positive integers. In general the number of partitions of m as an ordered sum of $k \leq m$ positive integers is $^{m-1}C_{k-1}$.

   If the above is specialised to $m = 2n + 1$ and $k = n + 1$ then the number of partitions of m as an ordered sum of $k \leq m$ *positive* integers is $^{2n}C_n$. We are of course interested in obtaining partitions that also contain zeros. This can be achieved by noting that each partition of m as an ordered sum of k positive integers gives rise to partition of $m - k$ as an ordered sum of k non-negative integers by subtracting 1 from every single term in the sum. For example, with $m = 11$ and $k = 6$, the partition $3 + 1 + 1 + 2 + 1 + 3$ gives rise to the partition $2 + 0 + 0 + 1 + 0 + 2$ of $11 - 6 = 5$ into an ordered sum of 6 non-negative integers. Thus the number of partitions of $(2n + 1) - (n + 1) = n$ as an ordered sum of $n + 1$ non-negative integers is the same as the number of partitions of $2n + 1$ as an ordered sum of $n + 1$ positive integers, which is $^{2n}C_n$.

   This result can also be proved by establishing a one-to-one correspondence between these partitions and the elements of a set that we already know enumerates to $^{2n}C_n$. This is a relatively common procedure in mathematics. For example, in order to obtain a one-to-one correspondence between the partitions of n as an ordered sum of $n + 1$ non-negative integers and the arrangements of n As and n Bs in a line, simply use mappings such as:

$$\text{AABBBABA} \quad \longleftrightarrow \quad 1 \underset{\uparrow}{} 1 \underset{\uparrow}{} 1 \quad 1 \quad 1 \quad 1 \underset{\uparrow}{} 1 \quad 1 \underset{\uparrow}{} 1$$

for which the position of the As in the arrangement on the left determine the position of the arrows in the spaces on the right (or vice versa).

   Here is another combinatorial interpretation of $^{2n}C_n$. Consider the 3×3 grid shown in Figure 3.1 on the next page. A path has been drawn from A at the bottom left corner of the grid to B at the top right-hand corner. Notice that this path from A to B uses only the lines on the grid, and

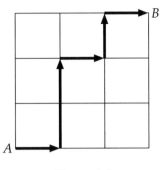

Figure 3.1

the direction of travel is either up or to the right. The number of such possible paths is equal to 20, which is $^6C_3$ (you should check this). In general there are $^{2n}C_n$ of these paths from A to B on an $n \times n$ grid. To see this, note that a path from A to B can be defined by giving a sequence of instructions as to how to proceed through the grid in terms of 'Ups' and 'Rights'.

For example, the sequence of instructions for the path shown in Figure 3.1 would be:

$$\text{Right} \quad \text{Up} \quad \text{Up} \quad \text{Right} \quad \text{Up} \quad \text{Right}.$$

Each path will be defined by a sequence of $2n$ instructions, half of which will be 'Rights' and half 'Ups'. Furthermore, each sequence of $2n$ instructions containing half 'Rights' and half 'Ups' will define a unique path from A to B on the grid. This establishes a one-to-one correspondence between the paths from A to B on the $n \times n$ grid and the arrangements of n 'Rights' and n 'Ups' in a line.

The combinatorial interpretation of $^{2n}C_n$ demonstrated via Figure 3.1 can be used to give a nice visual proof of Result 2.2 that

$$\sum_{k=0}^{n} \binom{n}{k}^2 = \binom{2n}{n}.$$

Consider an $n \times n$ grid for which the bottom left-hand corner A has coordinates $(0,0)$ and the top right-hand corner B has coordinates (n,n). We know that $^{2n}C_n$ enumerates all paths from A to B for which the direction of travel is either right or up. Any such path must go through some point on the 'opposite' diagonal defined by the coordinates $(0, n)$, $(1, n - 1)$, $(2, n - 2)$, ..., $(n, 0)$. The number of paths going from A to $(k, n - k)$ for some k with $0 \leq k \leq n$ is the number of distinct sequences consisting of k 'Rights' and $n - k$ 'Ups'. This is given by $^{k+(n-k)}C_k = {^nC_k}$. Similarly, the number of paths from $(k, n - k)$ to B is $^{(n-k)+k}C_{n-k} = {^nC_{n-k}}$. Thus the number of paths from A to B going through $(k, n - k)$ is

$$\binom{n}{k}\binom{n}{n-k} = \binom{n}{k}^2,$$

using the symmetry property (1.1). Result 2.2 then follows on summing over k (from $k = 0$ to $k = n$) in order to cover all $n + 1$ points on the 'opposite' diagonal.

Exercise 3

1. How many ways are there of partitioning

    (a) 19 into an ordered sum of 10 positive integers?

    (b) 12 into an ordered sum of 13 non-negative integers?

2. Consider the equation $u + v + w + x + y + z = 11$, where u, v, w, x, y and z are each positive integers. How many solutions (u, v, w, x, y, z) are there to this equation?

3. Find, to three significant figures, the number of solutions

    $$(a, b, c, d, \ldots, x, y, z)$$

    to the equation

    $$a + b + c + d + \cdots + x + y + z = 25,$$

    where $a, b, c, d, \ldots, x, y$ and z are each non-negative integers.

4. A fair cubical die with 1 to 6 on its faces is rolled five times and the numbers that come up are recorded. What is the probability that the sum of the numbers is 9?

5. (a) By considering paths from one corner to the opposite corner of a 7×7 grid, show that

$$\binom{3}{0}\binom{11}{7} + \binom{3}{1}\binom{11}{6} + \binom{3}{2}\binom{11}{5} + \binom{3}{3}\binom{11}{4} = \binom{14}{7}.$$

(b) Obtain a generalisation of this result.

Chapter 4

Obtaining the prime factorisation of ${}^{2n}C_n$

One way of expressing ${}^{2n}C_n$ as a product of primes for some particular value of n would be to write out

$$\binom{2n}{n} = \frac{2n \times (2n-1) \times (2n-2) \times \cdots \times (n+2) \times (n+1)}{n \times (n-1) \times (n-2) \times \times \cdots \times 2 \times 1}$$

for this value of n, and then go through some ad hoc cancelling process. This might be fine for small values of n but will be not appropriate for larger n, and besides, this rather non-systematic approach may not easily reveal any underlying structure or patterns.

Let us first consider a systematic way of obtaining the prime factorisation of $n!$ by looking at a particular example:

$$11! = 1 \times 2 \times 3 \times 4 \times 5 \times 6 \times 7 \times 8 \times 9 \times 10 \times 11.$$

What is the power of 2 in the prime factorisation of this number? Note that 2 is a factor of every second term in the above product (that is, the even-numbered terms in the product), $2^2 = 4$ is a factor of every fourth term (the multiples of 4) and $2^3 = 8$ is a factor of every eighth term (the multiples of 8). There are five even terms in the product, two multiples of 4 and one multiple of 8 so the overall contribution of these terms to the power of 2 in the prime factorisation of 11! is $5 + 2 + 1 = 8$. To see this, note that once the even terms have been counted then the multiples of 4 will have had one of their powers of 2 'used up', and once all the multiples of 4 have been accounted for then the multiples of 8 will have had two of their powers of 2 'used up'.

Using a similar argument it is clear, on noting that there are three multiples of 3 in the product and one multiple of $3^2 = 9$, that the power of 3 in the prime factorisation of 11! is $3 + 1 = 4$. Continuing this process with the primes 5, 7 and 11, we obtain

$$11! = 2^8 \times 3^4 \times 5^2 \times 7 \times 11.$$

It is possible to express the power of each prime appearing in the prime factorisation of 11! a little more succinctly by way of a formula that uses the symbol $\lfloor \ \rfloor$ to denote something called the *floor function*. The expression $\lfloor x \rfloor$ means the largest integer not exceeding x. So, for example,

$$\lfloor 3\tfrac{2}{3} \rfloor = 3, \ \lfloor 14 \rfloor = 14, \ \lfloor -3.1 \rfloor = -4 \text{ and } \lfloor \pi \rfloor = 3.$$

Task 4.1   A key property of the floor function used in many proofs is

$$\lfloor x \rfloor \leq x < \lfloor x \rfloor + 1.$$

Show that this is true for any real x, then draw a graph of $y = \lfloor x \rfloor$ to give a graphical demonstration of this result.

The expression $\lfloor \tfrac{n}{k} \rfloor$ gives the number of positive multiples of k no greater than n. For example, since $\lfloor \tfrac{257}{7} \rfloor = 36$ we know that there are thirty six multiples of 7 from 1 to 257 inclusive. Thus, on generalising the argument used to calculate the power of 2 in the prime factorisation of 11!, it follows that the exponent of p in the prime factorisation of $n!$ is given by

$$\sum_{j=1}^{\infty} \left\lfloor \frac{n}{p^j} \right\rfloor,$$

noting that there is no problem with the upper limit in this sum since $0 < \tfrac{n}{p^j} < 1$ when $p^j > n$, in which case $\left\lfloor \tfrac{n}{p^j} \right\rfloor = 0$. Going back to the example with $n = 11$ and $p = 2$, the exponent of 2 in the prime factorisation of 11! is

$$\sum_{j=1}^{\infty} \left\lfloor \frac{11}{2^j} \right\rfloor = \left\lfloor \frac{11}{2^1} \right\rfloor + \left\lfloor \frac{11}{2^2} \right\rfloor + \left\lfloor \frac{11}{2^3} \right\rfloor = 5 + 2 + 1 = 8.$$

To take a more adventurous example, let us calculate the power of 7 in the prime factorisation of 2506!. This is

$$\sum_{j=1}^{\infty} \left\lfloor \frac{2506}{7^j} \right\rfloor = \left\lfloor \frac{2506}{7^1} \right\rfloor + \left\lfloor \frac{2506}{7^2} \right\rfloor + \left\lfloor \frac{2506}{7^3} \right\rfloor + \left\lfloor \frac{2506}{7^4} \right\rfloor$$

$$= 358 + 51 + 7 + 1$$

$$= 417,$$

a result that would be extremely tedious to obtain by cancellation.

It is now very easy to calculate the prime factorisation of the factorial of any number. Here is the calculation for 25!:

$$\sum_{j=1}^{\infty} \left\lfloor \frac{25}{2^j} \right\rfloor = \left\lfloor \frac{25}{2^1} \right\rfloor + \left\lfloor \frac{25}{2^2} \right\rfloor + \left\lfloor \frac{25}{2^3} \right\rfloor + \left\lfloor \frac{25}{2^4} \right\rfloor = 12 + 6 + 3 + 1 = 22,$$

$$\sum_{j=1}^{\infty} \left\lfloor \frac{25}{3^j} \right\rfloor = \left\lfloor \frac{25}{3^1} \right\rfloor + \left\lfloor \frac{25}{3^2} \right\rfloor = 8 + 2 = 10,$$

$$\sum_{j=1}^{\infty} \left\lfloor \frac{25}{5^j} \right\rfloor = \left\lfloor \frac{25}{5^1} \right\rfloor + \left\lfloor \frac{25}{5^2} \right\rfloor = 5 + 1 = 6,$$

$$\sum_{j=1}^{\infty} \left\lfloor \frac{25}{7^j} \right\rfloor = \left\lfloor \frac{25}{7^1} \right\rfloor = 3,$$

and so on, to give

$$25! = 2^{22} \times 3^{10} \times 5^6 \times 7^3 \times 11^2 \times 13 \times 17 \times 19 \times 23.$$

Challenge 4.1   Calculate the number of zeros on the end of 1000!.

The systematic approach adopted above can clearly be generalised to determine the prime factorisation of $^{2n}C_n$:

Result 4.1 *The exponent of p appearing in the prime factorisation of $^{2n}C_n$ is given by*

$$\sum_{j=1}^{\infty} \left\lfloor \frac{2n}{p^j} \right\rfloor - \sum_{j=1}^{\infty} \left\lfloor \frac{n}{p^j} \right\rfloor - \sum_{j=1}^{\infty} \left\lfloor \frac{n}{p^j} \right\rfloor = \sum_{j=1}^{\infty} \left(\left\lfloor \frac{2n}{p^j} \right\rfloor - 2 \left\lfloor \frac{n}{p^j} \right\rfloor \right).$$

PROOF To see that this is in fact true use (1.5) and then note that the first sum on the left hand-side gives the exponent of p in the prime factorisation of $(2n)!$ while the following two sums each give the exponent of p in the prime factorisation of $n!$.   ❏

Result 4.1 can be used to obtain a useful result concerning the prime factorisation of $^{2n}C_n$, which will in turn be used to help prove a result in a later chapter concerning the distribution of primes. Before giving Result 4.2 we need to define a certain function on the primes.

Let p be a prime and n a positive integer. Then there exists a unique non-negative integer, m say, such that $p^m \leq 2n < p^{m+1}$. For example, if $p = 3$ and $n = 15$ then $m = 3$ since $3^3 \leq 30 < 3^4$. Now fix n and define the integer-valued function f on the primes as follows:

$f(p)$ is the unique non-negative integer satisfying $p^{f(p)} \leq 2n < p^{f(p)+1}$.

In other words f is a function whose domain is the primes and for which $f(p)$ is the highest power of p that does not exceed $2n$. Thus, since $2^4 \leq 30 < 2^5$, $f(2) = 4$ when $n = 15$. Similarly $f(3) = 3$, $f(5) = 2$, $f(7) = 1$ and so on.

Result 4.2

$$\binom{2n}{n} \,\Bigg|\, \prod_{p \leq 2n} p^{f(p)}.$$

PROOF From Result 4.1 the exponent of p in the prime factorisation of $^{2n}C_n$ is given by

$$\sum_{j=1}^{f(p)} \left(\left\lfloor \frac{2n}{p^j} \right\rfloor - 2 \left\lfloor \frac{n}{p^j} \right\rfloor \right),$$

but

$$\sum_{j=1}^{f(p)} \left(\left\lfloor \frac{2n}{p^j} \right\rfloor - 2 \left\lfloor \frac{n}{p^j} \right\rfloor \right) \leq \sum_{j=1}^{f(p)} 1 = f(p),$$

since the expression

$$\left\lfloor \frac{2n}{p^j} \right\rfloor - 2 \left\lfloor \frac{n}{p^j} \right\rfloor$$

is either 0 or 1 (using Result 4.3 below). The result then follows.   ❏

Result 4.3 *Let x be any real number. Then either* $\lfloor 2x \rfloor - 2\lfloor x \rfloor = 0$ *or* $\lfloor 2x \rfloor - 2\lfloor x \rfloor = 1$.

PROOF In order to prove this, note that $x = \lfloor x \rfloor + a$ for some a where either $0 \le a < \frac{1}{2}$ or $\frac{1}{2} \le a < 1$. In the former case

$$\lfloor 2x \rfloor - 2\lfloor x \rfloor = \lfloor 2\lfloor x \rfloor + 2a \rfloor - 2\lfloor \lfloor x \rfloor + a \rfloor = 2\lfloor x \rfloor - 2\lfloor x \rfloor = 0,$$

while in the latter case

$$\lfloor 2x \rfloor - 2\lfloor x \rfloor = \lfloor 2\lfloor x \rfloor + 2a \rfloor - 2\lfloor \lfloor x \rfloor + a \rfloor = (2\lfloor x \rfloor + 1) - 2\lfloor x \rfloor = 1,$$

as required. ❑

Challenge 4.2　Let p be a prime. Show that when n is added to itself in base p the number of carries required is equal to the power of p in the prime factorisation of $^{2n}C_n$ (see Appendix C which describes how to express numbers in bases other than decimal).

Let us illustrate this by an example. The number 14 becomes 11010 and 112 when written in binary and ternary respectively. Now add 14 to itself in these bases to obtain

$$
\begin{array}{r}
1\,1\,1\,0 \\
+\,1\,1\,1\,0 \\
\hline
1\,1\,1\,0\,0 \\
\hline
1\,1\,1
\end{array}
\quad \text{and} \quad
\begin{array}{r}
1\,1\,2 \\
+\,1\,1\,2 \\
\hline
1\,0\,0\,1 \\
\hline
1\,1\,1
\end{array}
$$

where the digits at the bottom signify the carries. The prime factorisation of $^{28}C_{14}$ is given by

$$^{28}C_{14} = 2^3 \times 3^3 \times 5^2 \times 17 \times 19 \times 23.$$

Note that three carries were required in the addition base 2 and also in the addition base 3, and that 2 and 3 both appear to the power three in the prime factorisation of $^{28}C_{14}$. Next, consider the situation in base 5, where 14 becomes 24. Adding 14 to itself in base 5 gives

$$
\begin{array}{r}
2\,4 \\
+\,2\,4 \\
\hline
1\,0\,3 \\
\hline
1\,1
\end{array}
$$

and the two carries match the power of 5 in the prime factorisation of $^{28}C_{14}$.

Exercise 4

1. Evaluate the following numerical expressions involving the floor function, giving your answers as rational numbers:

    (a) $\lfloor 7\pi \rfloor - \lfloor 6\pi \rfloor$ (b) $\lfloor 8\pi \rfloor - \lfloor 7\pi \rfloor$ (c) $\frac{\lfloor 7\pi \rfloor}{7 \lfloor \pi \rfloor}$ (d) $\frac{\lfloor 8\pi \rfloor}{8 \lfloor \pi \rfloor}$.

2. Obtain the prime factorisations of

    (a) 189 336   (b) 31!   (c) $^{40}C_{20}$.

3. Let $n = 6$ and, for this value of n, let $f(p)$ be the function defined immediately before Result 4.2.

    (a) Work out $f(2)$, $f(3)$, $f(5)$, $f(7)$ and $f(11)$.

    (b) Now calculate $^{12}C_6$.

    (c) Use your answers to (a) and (b) to demonstrate the truth of Result 4.2 for the case $n = 6$.

4. Simplify the following expression as much as possible, given that both k and m are integers:

$$\left\lfloor \frac{k+m}{2} \right\rfloor + \left\lfloor \frac{k-m+1}{2} \right\rfloor.$$

5. Find an expression, in terms of k, for the number of zeros on the end of $\left(5^k\right)!$.

6. Use your answer to 2(b) to obtain the number of zeros on the end of 31! when it is expressed in base

    (a) 7   (b) 14   (c) 8   (d) 10 000

    (Again, see Appendix C for details on how to express numbers in different bases.)

7. (a) Let S be the set $\{0, 1, 2, 3, \ldots, 2^{2n} - 1\}$. An integer is chosen at random from S and written in binary. What is the probability that it contains exactly n 1s?

    (b) Let T be the set $\{0, 1, 2, 3, \ldots, 10^{2n} - 1\}$. An integer is chosen at random from T (and left in decimal). What is the probability that it contains exactly n 8s?

Chapter 5

Using integrals to estimate $^{2n}C_n$

Suppose that we want to have an idea of the size of $\binom{200}{100}$, for example. Although most scientific calculators have an ^nC_r button, they will not permit the calculation of binomial coefficients with n and r this large. In fact, my calculator gave error messages for $^{200}C_r$ when $45 \le r \le 155$ and also for $^{2n}C_n$ when $n \ge 53$. An error message was also obtained for $n!$ with $n \ge 70$. We are thus left with the very tedious calculation

$$\frac{200 \times 199 \times 198 \times \cdots \times 101}{100 \times 99 \times 98 \times \cdots \times 1},$$

noting that, because of the size of the numbers involved, the calculator will not allow us first to calculate the numerator and then divide by the denominator (thereby making the calculation all the more tedious!). In Chapter 2 (Result 2.5) upper and lower bounds for $^{2n}C_n$ were obtained in terms of some particularly simple functions of n:

$$\frac{2^{2n-1}}{n} < \binom{2n}{n} < 2^{2n} \text{ for } n \ge 2.$$

Using this result gives

$$8.03 \times 10^{57} < \binom{200}{100} < 1.61 \times 10^{60},$$

which, unfortunately, does not locate $^{200}C_{100}$ to any great degree of precision.

At various points on our tour along the backbone of Pascal's triangle we shall find it expedient to have an approximation to $^{2n}C_n$ in terms of a relatively simple function of n. Although the above bounds will be sufficient in some cases there will also be occasions when considerably more accurate approximations are required. In this chapter we derive what is known as an *asymptotic relation* for $^{2n}C_n$, providing 'good' information on how $^{2n}C_n$ behaves as n becomes large ('good' in the sense described in the following paragraph).

Suppose that a function $f(n)$ can be found such that

$$\frac{^{2n}C_n}{f(n)} \to 1 \text{ as } n \to \infty.$$

We say in this case that $f(n)$ provides us with an asymptotic estimate for $^{2n}C_n$ and write

$$^{2n}C_n \sim f(n),$$

where the wavy line '$\sim$' means "approximately equal to" in the sense that the ratio between $^{2n}C_n$ and $f(n)$ tends to 1 as n increases without limit.

A mathematical statement, such as the one above, providing information on the behaviour of a function as n gets large is called an asymptotic relation. Here is a simple example to illustrate the key ideas. Although the function $F(n)$ defined by

$$F(n) = \sum_{k=1}^{n} k$$

does actually have the exact result $F(n) = \frac{1}{2}n(n+1)$, we might want an even simpler statement of the approximate behaviour of this function as n gets large. It is in fact possible to write $F(n) \sim \frac{1}{2}n^2$ since

$$\frac{\frac{1}{2}n^2}{\frac{1}{2}n(n+1)} = \frac{n}{n+1} \to 1 \text{ as } n \to \infty.$$

Note that this does *not* necessarily say that $F(n)$ gets closer to $\frac{1}{2}n^2$ as n increases. Indeed, some quick calculations should convince you that the larger n becomes the *further* $F(n)$ tends to be from $\frac{1}{2}n^2$. What the relation does say, however, is that the relative error in using $\frac{1}{2}n^2$ for $F(n)$ tends to zero as n tends to infinity.

In this chapter we shall use the family of integrals defined by

$$S_n = \int_0^{\frac{\pi}{2}} \sin^n x \, dx,$$

where n is a non-negative integer, to obtain an asymptotic relation for $^{2n}C_n$. The first step is to derive the following result connecting $^{2n}C_n$ and S_{2n}:

Result 5.1

$$\binom{2n}{n} = \frac{2^{2n+1}}{\pi} S_{2n}.$$

PROOF Using integration by parts with

$$u = \sin^{n-1} x \text{ and } \frac{dv}{dx} = \sin x$$

gives

$$S_n = \left[-\cos x \sin^{n-1} x \right]_0^{\frac{\pi}{2}} - \int_0^{\frac{\pi}{2}} (-\cos x) \left((n-1) \cos x \sin^{n-2} x \right) dx$$

$$= (n-1) \int_0^{\frac{\pi}{2}} \cos^2 x \sin^{n-2} x \, dx$$

$$= (n-1) \int_0^{\frac{\pi}{2}} (1 - \sin^2 x) \sin^{n-2} x \, dx$$

$$= (n-1) \int_0^{\frac{\pi}{2}} \sin^{n-2} x \, dx - (n-1) \int_0^{\frac{\pi}{2}} \sin^n x \, dx$$

$$= (n-1)S_{n-2} - (n-1)S_n,$$

leading to the recurrence relation

$$S_n = \frac{n-1}{n} S_{n-2}. \tag{5.1}$$

Now

$$S_0 = \int_0^{\frac{\pi}{2}} dx = \frac{\pi}{2},$$

so

$$S_2 = \frac{2-1}{2} S_{2-2} = \frac{1}{2} S_0 = \frac{1}{2} \times \frac{\pi}{2},$$
$$S_4 = \frac{4-1}{4} S_{4-2} = \frac{3}{4} S_2 = \frac{3}{4} \times \frac{1}{2} \times \frac{\pi}{2},$$
$$S_6 = \frac{6-1}{6} S_{6-2} = \frac{5}{6} S_4 = \frac{5}{6} \times \frac{3}{4} \times \frac{1}{2} \times \frac{\pi}{2}$$

and in general

$$S_{2n} = \frac{2n-1}{2n} \times \frac{2n-3}{2(n-1)} \times \cdots \times \frac{1}{2} \times \frac{\pi}{2}$$

$$= \frac{(2n-1) \times (2n-3) \times \cdots \times 1}{2^n n!} \times \frac{\pi}{2}$$

$$= \frac{2n \times 2(n-1) \times \cdots \times 2}{2n \times 2(n-1) \times \cdots \times 2} \times \frac{(2n-1) \times (2n-3) \times \cdots \times 1}{2^n n!} \times \frac{\pi}{2}$$

$$= \frac{1}{2^n n!} \times \frac{2n \times (2n-1) \times 2(n-1) \times (2n-3) \times \cdots \times 2 \times 1}{2^n n!} \times \frac{\pi}{2}$$

$$= \frac{(2n)!}{2^{2n}(n!)^2} \times \frac{\pi}{2}$$

$$= \frac{\pi}{2^{2n+1}} \binom{2n}{n},$$

as required.   □

Challenge 5.1   Show that

$$S_{2n} = \int_0^\infty \frac{1}{(x^2+1)^{n+1}} \, dx$$

and hence that

$$\binom{2n}{n} = \frac{2^{2n+1}}{\pi} \int_0^\infty \frac{1}{(x^2+1)^{n+1}} \, dx.$$

The recurrence relation (5.1) can also be used to evaluate the odd-numbered terms of the sequence $\{S_n\}$. Since

$$S_1 = \int_0^{\frac{\pi}{2}} \sin x \, dx = 1,$$

it follows that

$$S_3 = \frac{3-1}{3} S_{3-2} = \frac{2}{3} S_1 = \frac{2}{3},$$

$$S_5 = \frac{5-1}{5} S_{5-2} = \frac{4}{5} S_3 = \frac{4}{5} \times \frac{2}{3}$$

and so on.

Now note that

$$S_0 S_1 = \tfrac{\pi}{2},$$
$$S_1 S_2 = \tfrac{1}{2} \times \tfrac{\pi}{2},$$
$$S_2 S_3 = \left(\tfrac{1}{2} \times \tfrac{\pi}{2}\right) \times \tfrac{2}{3} = \tfrac{1}{3} \times \tfrac{\pi}{2},$$
$$S_3 S_4 = \tfrac{2}{3} \times \left(\tfrac{1}{2} \times \tfrac{3}{4} \times \tfrac{\pi}{2}\right) = \tfrac{1}{4} \times \tfrac{\pi}{2},$$

which does indeed generalise (check!) to

$$n S_{n-1} S_n = \tfrac{\pi}{2}. \tag{5.2}$$

Using (5.1) and (5.2) it is possible to establish a result giving us information on the behaviour of S_n as n becomes large:

Result 5.2
$$S_n \sqrt{n} \to \sqrt{\tfrac{\pi}{2}} \text{ as } n \to \infty.$$

PROOF On considering (5.1) it is clear that

$$\frac{S_n}{S_{n-2}} \to 1 \text{ as } n \to \infty.$$

It then follows, since $S_n < S_{n-1} < S_{n-2}$, that

$$\frac{S_n}{S_{n-1}} \to 1 \text{ as } n \to \infty. \tag{5.3}$$

Next, from (5.2) we obtain

$$n S_{n-1} S_n \times \frac{S_n}{S_{n-1}} = \frac{\pi}{2} \times \frac{S_n}{S_{n-1}},$$

which, on using (5.3), gives

$$n S_n^2 \to \tfrac{\pi}{2} \text{ as } n \to \infty.$$

Noting that S_n is always positive, the result follows. ❑

We now have all the results needed in order to obtain an asymptotic relation for $^{2n}C_n$:

Result 5.3

$$\binom{2n}{n} \sim \frac{2^{2n}}{\sqrt{n\pi}}.$$

PROOF First, a rearrangement of Result 5.1 gives

$$\frac{\pi\sqrt{2n}}{2^{2n+1}}\binom{2n}{n} = S_{2n}\sqrt{2n}.$$

Using this in conjunction with Result 5.2 gives

$$\frac{\pi\sqrt{2n}}{2^{2n+1}}\binom{2n}{n} \rightarrow \sqrt{\tfrac{\pi}{2}} \text{ as } n \rightarrow \infty,$$

from which the asymptotic relation follows. ❏

Task 5.1 Compare the numerical values of $^{2n}C_n$ and $\frac{2^{2n}}{\sqrt{n\pi}}$ for several values of n. On the basis of this rather flimsy numerical evidence, would you conjecture that $^{2n}C_n$ and $\frac{2^{2n}}{\sqrt{n\pi}}$ get closer as n increases, or further apart? The answer is that they get further apart as n increases, giving another illustration of the fact that $f(n) \sim g(n)$ does not necessarily mean that $f(n)$ and $g(n)$ get closer and closer as n increases without bound.

We shall have cause to use Result 5.3 at various points throughout this book. In order to gain a little more familiarity with this result here is another proof of Result 2.1 concerning the rate of growth of $^{2n}C_n$. Using Result 5.3 with $^{2n}C_n$ and $^{2(n+1)}C_{n+1}$ gives

$$\binom{2(n+1)}{n+1} \div \binom{2n}{n} \sim \frac{2^{2(n+1)}}{\sqrt{(n+1)\pi}} \div \frac{2^{2n}}{\sqrt{n\pi}} = 2^2\sqrt{\frac{n}{n+1}}.$$

Then, since $\sqrt{\frac{n}{n+1}} \rightarrow 1$ as $n \rightarrow \infty$, we see that $\frac{^{2(n+1)}C_{n+1}}{^{2n}C_n} \rightarrow 4$ as $n \rightarrow \infty$.

Research Activity 5.1 Find out about *Wallis' product* and show that the evaluation of it is equivalent to Result 5.3.

Challenge 5.2   Consider the central binomial coefficients of the form

$$t(m) = \binom{2 \times 10^m}{10^m}, \quad m \geq 0.$$

You will find that $t(0) = 2$ and $t(1) = 184\,756$, having 1 decimal digit and 6 decimal digits respectively. Your calculator will probably not allow you to calculate $t(2)$, but if it did you would find that $t(2)$ had 59 decimal digits. Using $D[x]$ to denote the number of decimal digits in x we have that $D[t(3)] = 601$, $D[t(4)] = 6\,019$ and $D[t(5)] = 60\,204$.

The interesting thing here is that $D[t(m)]$ appears to give the digits after the decimal point of $\log_{10} 4 = 0.6020599\ldots$ to greater and greater accuracy as m increases. Show that this conjecture is in fact true. You might find Result 5.3 useful.

Finally, it is worth mentioning a result known as *Stirling's formula*, which provides an asymptotic estimate for $n!$. It is named after the Scottish mathematician James Stirling (1692-1770), who discovered it some time before 1730. It is interesting also to note that Stirling made several attempts to generalise $n!$ to non-integer values of n. He did make some progress in this area, although was not entirely successful. Leonhard Euler was the first person to find the appropriate generalisation. His idea appears in a letter he wrote to another mathematician in 1729. The generalisation of $n!$ to non-integer values of n is something we shall consider in a later chapter. Unfortunately, a proof of Stirling's formula is beyond the scope of this book, so it merely stated as Result 5.4:

Result 5.4

$$n! \sim \sqrt{2\pi n} \left(\frac{n}{e}\right)^n.$$

Research Activity 5.2   Find out what you can about Stirling's formula and its uses in mathematics. If possible, locate a proof (one is given in [10] for example) in order to see which of the mathematical ideas and techniques involved are already familiar to you and which of them you can make neither head nor tail of. As you progress mathematically you will find it heartening to revisit the proof every now and again. Each time you will notice a gradual improvement in both your understanding of the fine detail and your appreciation of the overall structure.

Exercise 5

1. (a) Use Result 5.3 to obtain estimates for

    (i) $^{10}C_5$ (ii) $^{20}C_{10}$ (iii) $^{40}C_{20}$

    (b) Now, with the help of the $^{n}C_r$ button on your calculator, work
    out the absolute and relative error in using the approximation
    for each of these numbers.

2. Put the following in order according to their size, largest first:

$$\binom{200}{100} \qquad \sqrt{\binom{400}{200}} \qquad \binom{100}{50}^2 \qquad 46! \qquad ((3!)!)!$$

3. Show that

$$\binom{2n}{n} + \binom{2(n+1)}{n+1} \sim \frac{5 \times 2^{2n}}{\sqrt{n\pi}}.$$

4. Use Stirling's formula given in Result 5.4 to derive the asymptotic
    estimate for $\binom{2n}{n}$ given in Result 5.3.

5. Let $S(n) = 1^2 + 2^2 + 3^2 + \cdots + n^2$. Prove that $S(n) \sim \frac{n^3}{3}$.

6. (a) Since

$$\frac{(n+1)!}{n!} = n+1,$$

    we would certainly expect that when we divide the estimate
    for $(n+1)!$ using Stirling's formula by the estimate for $n!$ the
    answer should be close to $n+1$. Show that it is in fact

$$\frac{n+1}{e} \left(\frac{n+1}{n}\right)^{n+\frac{1}{2}}.$$

    (b) Prove that the above expression does behave approximately as
    $n+1$ as $n \to \infty$.

7. What familiar number does

$$\frac{1}{n} \left(\frac{\text{product of first } n \text{ even numbers}}{\text{product of first } n \text{ odd numbers}}\right)^2$$

    approach as $n \to \infty$?
    Why is this a poor method of trying to calculate it?

8. (a) Show that

$$\frac{4k-3}{4k+1} < \left(\frac{2k-1}{2k}\right)^2 \le \frac{3k-2}{3k+1} \text{ for } k \ge 1.$$

(b) Deduce that

$$\frac{1}{\sqrt{4n+1}} < \frac{1 \times 3 \times 5 \times \cdots \times (2n-1)}{2 \times 4 \times 6 \times \cdots \times 2n} \le \frac{1}{\sqrt{3n+1}} \text{ for } n \ge 1,$$

and hence that

$$\frac{2^{2n}}{\sqrt{4n+1}} < \binom{2n}{n} < \frac{2^{2n}}{\sqrt{3n+1}}.$$

(Note that although the above result is not as good as Result 5.3, it is a considerable improvement on Result 2.5).

Chapter 6

Series involving $^{2n}C_n$

For reasons that will soon become apparent, we first obtain a rearrangement of $^{2n}C_n$:

$$
\begin{aligned}
\binom{2n}{n} &= \frac{1 \times 2 \times 3 \times 4 \times \cdots \times (2n-1) \times 2n}{(n!)^2} \\
&= \frac{(2 \times 1) \times (2 \times 2) \times \cdots \times (2n) \times 1 \times 3 \times \cdots \times (2n-1)}{(n!)^2} \\
&= \frac{n!}{n!} \times \frac{2^n \times 1 \times 3 \times \cdots \times (2n-1)}{n!} \\
&= \frac{2^n \times 1 \times 3 \times \cdots \times (2n-1)}{n!} \\
&= \frac{\left(-\frac{1}{2}\right)^n \times (-4)^n \times 1 \times 3 \times \cdots \times (2n-1)}{n!} \\
&= \frac{\left(-\frac{1}{2}\right)\left(-\frac{3}{2}\right)\cdots\left(-\frac{2n-1}{2}\right)}{n!} \times (-4)^n.
\end{aligned}
\tag{6.1}
$$

If you have ever used the generalised binomial theorem (see Appendix B) to expand functions as infinite power series, then the form of (6.1) above might look vaguely familiar. Indeed, it is actually the coefficient of x^n in the binomial expansion of

$$
G(x) = \frac{1}{\sqrt{1-4x}}, \quad \text{where } |x| < \tfrac{1}{4},
$$

the first few terms of which are given by

$$G(x) = 1 + \frac{\left(-\frac{1}{2}\right)}{1!}(-4x) + \frac{\left(-\frac{1}{2}\right)\left(-\frac{3}{2}\right)}{2!}(-4x)^2$$
$$+ \frac{\left(-\frac{1}{2}\right)\left(-\frac{3}{2}\right)\left(-\frac{5}{2}\right)}{3!}(-4x)^3 + \cdots$$

Thus we have a function which, when expanded as a power series, has coefficients that are the central binomial coefficients. Such a function is called a *generating function* for the sequence $\{^{2n}C_n\}$, and it is now possible to write

$$\sum_{k=0}^{\infty}\binom{2k}{k}x^k = \frac{1}{\sqrt{1-4x}}, \quad |x| < \tfrac{1}{4}. \tag{6.2}$$

This allows us to obtain numerical identities such as

$$\sum_{k=0}^{\infty}\frac{1}{8^k}\binom{2k}{k} = \frac{1}{\sqrt{1-4\times\frac{1}{8}}} = \sqrt{2}.$$

Also, since

$$\frac{d}{dx}\left[\sum_{k=0}^{\infty}\binom{2k}{k}x^k\right] = \sum_{k=0}^{\infty}kx^{k-1}\binom{2k}{k}$$

and

$$\frac{d}{dx}\left[\frac{1}{\sqrt{1-4x}}\right] = \frac{2}{\sqrt{(1-4x)^3}},$$

we are able to obtain results such as

$$\sum_{k=0}^{\infty}\frac{k}{8^{k-1}}\binom{2k}{k} = \frac{2}{\sqrt{\left(1-4\times\frac{1}{8}\right)^3}} = 4\sqrt{2}.$$

Research Activity 6.1   Find out how to represent certain functions by power series, and when these representations are valid. The above example supposes that it is valid to differentiate an infinite power series term by term. To show that we are actually allowed to do this would take us a little beyond the scope of our current work. Perhaps this is something that you might also like to look up.

We have already seen that the asymptotic formula for $^{2n}C_n$ given as Result 5.3 establishes a link (if seemingly a somewhat tenuous one) between π and the central binomial coefficients. However, there also exist amazing relationships between these numbers such as:

$$\frac{\pi}{3} = 1 + \frac{1}{4^2 \times 3}\binom{2}{1} + \frac{1}{4^4 \times 5}\binom{4}{2} + \frac{1}{4^6 \times 7}\binom{6}{3} + \cdots$$

$$= \sum_{k=0}^{\infty} \frac{1}{4^{2k}(2k+1)}\binom{2k}{k}$$

and

$$\pi = \frac{2}{{}^0C_0} + \frac{2^2}{3 \times 2\,C_1} + \frac{2^3}{5 \times 4\,C_2} + \frac{2^4}{7 \times 6\,C_3} + \cdots$$

$$= \sum_{k=0}^{\infty} \frac{2^{k+1}}{{}^{2k}C_k(2k+1)}.$$

Results like these are rather intriguing and you should want to know how they are derived. The first of these results is proved here, while the second appears as a Challenge in Chapter 10 for you to tackle at your leisure.

Result 6.1

$$\frac{\pi}{3} = \sum_{k=0}^{\infty} \frac{1}{4^{2k}(2k+1)}\binom{2k}{k}.$$

PROOF We start by replacing x with x^2 in (6.2) and integrating both sides with respect to x from $x = 0$ to $x = \frac{1}{4}$ to give

$$\int_0^{\frac{1}{4}} \left[\sum_{k=0}^{\infty} \binom{2k}{k} x^{2k}\right] dx = \int_0^{\frac{1}{4}} \frac{dx}{\sqrt{1-4x^2}}. \tag{6.3}$$

Then, assuming that the sum on the left of (6.3) can be integrated term by term, we obtain the following:

$$\left[\sum_{k=0}^{\infty} \frac{x^{2k+1}}{2k+1}\binom{2k}{k}\right]_0^{\frac{1}{4}} = \frac{1}{2}\int_0^{\frac{1}{2}} \frac{du}{\sqrt{1-u^2}}$$

$$= \frac{1}{2}\left[\sin^{-1} u\right]_0^{\frac{1}{2}}$$

$$= \frac{\pi}{12},$$

where the substitution $u = 2x$ has been used to evaluate the integral on the right of (6.3).

Now

$$\left[\sum_{k=0}^{\infty} \frac{x^{2k+1}}{2k+1} \binom{2k}{k}\right]_0^{\frac{1}{4}} = \sum_{k=0}^{\infty} \frac{1}{4^{2k+1}(2k+1)} \binom{2k}{k}$$

$$= \frac{1}{4} \sum_{k=0}^{\infty} \frac{1}{4^{2k}(2k+1)} \binom{2k}{k}.$$

and the result follows.   ❏

Deciding whether or not an infinite series can be integrated or differentiated term by term is beyond the scope of this book. The conditions involved are, in both cases, taught in analysis courses at university.

Exercise 6

1. Evaluate the following:

(a) $\displaystyle\sum_{k=0}^{\infty} \left(\frac{1}{5}\right)^{k+1} \binom{2k}{k}$ (b) $\displaystyle\sum_{k=0}^{\infty} \frac{k}{(-12)^{k-1}} \binom{2k}{k}$

(c) $\displaystyle\sum_{k=0}^{\infty} \frac{3k-1}{8^k} \binom{2k}{k}$.

2. By taking the second derivative with respect to x of both sides of (6.2) evaluate

(a) $\displaystyle\sum_{k=0}^{\infty} \frac{k(k-1)}{8^{k-2}} \binom{2k}{k}$ (b) $\displaystyle\sum_{k=0}^{\infty} \frac{k^2}{8^k} \binom{2k}{k}$.

3. Let m be a non-negative integer. Show that

$$\sum_{k=m+1}^{\infty} \frac{k(k-1)(k-2)\dots(k-m)}{8^k} \binom{2k}{k}$$

$$= \frac{1 \times 3 \times 5 \times \cdots \times (2m+1)}{2^{m+1}} \sqrt{2}.$$

4. Evaluate

$$\sum_{k=0}^{\infty} \frac{1}{9^{k+1}(k+1)}\binom{2k}{k}.$$

Chapter 7

The Catalan numbers

This sequence of numbers, though not named after him, seems to have been discovered by the amazingly prolific Swiss mathematician Leonhard Euler (1707-1783). They appeared when he was investigating the number of ways, T_n say, of splitting a regular n-sided polygon up into $n - 2$ triangles using non-intersecting diagonals of the polygon. This process is illustrated in Figure 7.1. It is worth noting that although the first shape in

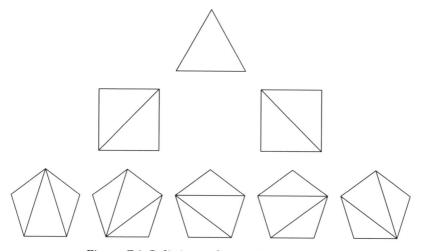

Figure 7.1: Splitting polygons into triangles

the third row of Figure 7.1, for example, can be rotated to give the second shape in this row, these are regarded as being distinct ways of splitting the pentagon up into triangles.

From Figure 7.1 it can be seen that this sequence starts $1, 2, 5, \ldots$. Let us define the *Catalan numbers* C_n by $C_0 = 1$ and $C_n = T_{n+2}$ for $n \geq 1$. Thus far we know that $C_1 = 1, C_2 = 2$ and $C_3 = 5$.

Task 7.1   Find C_4 by drawing all the possible ways in which a regular hexagon can be split up into 4 triangles using non-intersecting diagonals.

The above definition of C_n lends itself to finding a general recurrence relation for these numbers, but let us first consider a specific example. Figure 7.2 shows an octagon with its vertices labelled from 1 to 8. Suppose

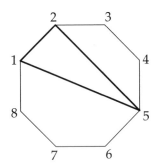

Figure 7.2: Splitting an octagon into triangles

that this octagon has been partitioned into 6 triangles by drawing in 5 non-intersecting diagonals. For any such partition the edge of the octagon connecting vertex 1 to vertex 2 will be an edge of one of the partitioning triangles. Figure 7.2 exhibits a partitioning triangle with vertices 1, 2 and 5. Now let us consider all possible partitions containing this particular triangle. The quadrilateral with vertices 2, 3, 4 and 5 can be partitioned into triangles in C_2 ways while the pentagon with vertices 1, 5, 6, 7 and 8 can be partitioned into triangles in C_3 ways. There are thus $C_2 C_3$ ways of partitioning the octagon into triangles such that one of the triangles is as shown in Figure 7.2. This can be done for all triangles with vertices 1, 2 and k, for $k = 3, 4, 5, 6, 7, 8$. Going through this process enumerates all possible partitions (although you ought to convince yourself that there will be no repeats) so that

$$C_6 = C_5 + C_1 C_4 + C_2 C_3 + C_3 C_2 + C_4 C_1 + C_5.$$

Let us now consider a regular $(n + 2)$-sided polygon with its vertices labelled in order from 1 to $n + 2$. The above method for enumerating the number of ways that it can be partitioned into n triangles using $n - 1$ non-intersecting diagonals clearly generalises, on remembering that $C_0 = 1$ by definition, to give

$$C_n = C_0 C_{n-1} + C_1 C_{n-2} + C_2 C_{n-3} + \cdots + C_{n-2} C_1 + C_{n-1} C_0$$
$$= \sum_{k=1}^{n} C_{k-1} C_{n-k}. \tag{7.1}$$

If you are wondering how the Catalan numbers are connected to the central binomial coefficients, this will become apparent in due course. First, however, we demonstrate a particularly fascinating aspect of the Catalan numbers, namely that they have many different combinatorial interpretations. Furthermore, it is not at all obvious in some cases that different interpretations will generate the same sequence of numbers.

The last statement can be illustrated by considering a particular election scenario involving just two candidates. Imagine that you have put yourself forward as a parliamentary candidate (candidate a) for your local constituency and that you are fighting against just one other candidate (candidate b). The day of the election arrives and it turns out that the result is a dead-heat, with each of you receiving n votes. Say also that a running total of the votes had been kept throughout the day and it was found that your running total at any point was always at least as large as that of candidate b. Then, with these conditions, the number of possible orders in which the $2n$ votes can be cast is defined to be V_n for $n \geq 1$ (we also define V_0 to be 1). We shall call such sequences of votes *allowed voting patterns*.

For example, if six votes were cast in total there are just 5 allowed voting patterns, where A and B represent single votes for candidate a and candidate b respectively:

AAABBB   AABABB   AABBAB   ABAABB   ABABAB

while if eight votes were cast then there are 14 possible allowed voting patterns:

AAAABBBB   AAABABBB   AAABBABB   AAABBBAB   AABAABBB
AABABABB   AABABBAB   AABBAABB   AABBABAB   ABAAABBB
ABAABABB   ABAABBAB   ABABAABB   ABABABAB

We now establish a recurrence relation for V_n. Let us assume once more that you received the first vote. Suppose that the very first time that you and candidate b have received exactly the same number of votes occurs after $2k$ votes have been cast. Then candidate b must have received the $(2k)$th vote. Furthermore, from the second vote to the $(2k-1)$th vote there will have been $2(k-1)$ votes cast such that both of you received exactly $k-1$ votes each and for which you were never behind candidate b. The final $2(n-k)$ votes will be such that you and candidate b receive the same number of votes with you never being behind candidate b. The diagram below gives a visual interpretation of the situation:

A	A . . . . B	B	A . . . . B
first vote	next $2(k-1)$ votes	$(2k)$th vote	final $2n-2k$ votes

Note that there are V_{k-1} possible arrangements for the second to the $(2k-1)$th votes, given by the second block above and that there are V_{n-k} possibilities for the final block. Therefore there are $V_{k-1}V_{n-k}$ possible allowed voting patterns for which the first time that candidate b has caught up with you occurs after $2k$ votes have been cast. To cover all possibilities we sum from $k=1$ to $k=n$ to give

$$V_n = \sum_{k=1}^{n} V_{k-1}V_{n-k}.$$

This establishes that our definition of V_n leads to the same recurrence relation as that obtained from partitioning polygons into triangles. It is then possible to write $V_n = C_n$, noting that the initial conditions for both recurrence relations do indeed match.

It has already been shown in Chapter 3 that one interpretation of $^{2n}C_n$ is the number of paths from the bottom left-hand corner to the top right hand corner of an $n \times n$ grid such that movement is restricted to 'right' or 'up'. Another example of such a path for $n = 5$ is given in Figure 7.3. We may in fact interpret C_n as enumerating the subset of these paths which

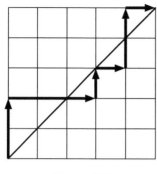

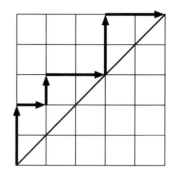

Figure 7.3   Figure 7.4

do not dip below the diagonal joining the opposite corners of the grid. To see this, consider the voting scenario definition of the Catalan numbers in which C_n enumerates all possible sequences of n As and n Bs such that the number of As to any point is never exceeded by the number of Bs to that point. If, for such a sequence, we assign 'up' to each A and 'right' to each B then we end up with a sequence of instructions that get us from the bottom left-hand corner to the top right-hand corner of the grid without dipping below the diagonal joining these corners. There is a one-to-one correspondence between the allowed voting patterns and these restricted paths across the grid. For example, the sequence AABABBAABB generates the path shown for the 5×5 grid shown in Figure 7.4.

Thus far a recurrence relation for the Catalan numbers has emerged, but no formula. In order to remedy this situation we now find a generating function for the Catalan numbers (using two different methods):

Result 7.1 *Let $H(x)$ be the generating function for the Catalan numbers. Then*

$$H(x) = \frac{1 - \sqrt{1 - 4x}}{2x}.$$

FIRST PROOF Integrating the generating function for the central binomial coefficients (6.2) gives

$$\int_0^x \frac{1}{\sqrt{1 - 4t}}\, dt = \left[-\frac{\sqrt{1 - 4t}}{2} \right]_0^x = \frac{1 - \sqrt{1 - 4x}}{2}.$$

Also

$$\int_0^x \left\{ \binom{0}{0} + \binom{2}{1}t + \binom{4}{2}t^2 + \ldots \right\} dt$$

$$= \binom{0}{0}x + \binom{2}{1}\frac{x^2}{2} + \binom{4}{2}\frac{x^3}{3} + \cdots$$

$$= x\left[\binom{0}{0} + \binom{2}{1}\frac{x}{2} + \binom{4}{2}\frac{x^2}{3} + \cdots \right]$$

$$= xH(x),$$

assuming that this term-by-term integration is valid. This shows that

$$H(x) = \frac{1 - \sqrt{1 - 4x}}{2x}.$$

❏

SECOND PROOF For the second derivation of the generating function for the Catalan numbers we can utilise the Catalan recurrence relation (7.1). To this end, let us start once more by defining

$$H(x) = C_0 + C_1 x + C_2 x^2 + \cdots = \sum_{k=0}^{\infty} C_k x^k.$$

The recurrence relation

$$C_n = \sum_{k=1}^{n} C_{k-1} C_{n-k}$$

is very suggestive as to how to proceed, since

$$[H(x)]^2 = [C_0 + C_1 x + C_2 x^2 + \cdots]^2$$

$$= C_0 \times C_0 + (C_0 \times C_1 + C_1 \times C_0)x$$

$$\qquad + (C_0 \times C_2 + C_1 \times C_1 + C_2 \times C_0)x^2 + \cdots$$

$$= C_1 + C_2 x + C_3 x^2 + \cdots$$

$$= \sum_{k=0}^{\infty} C_{k+1} x^k.$$

Thus

$$x[H(x)]^2 - x\sum_{k=0}^{\infty} C_{k+1}x^k - \sum_{k=0}^{\infty} C_{k+1}x^{k+1} = \sum_{k=1}^{\infty} C_k x^k = H(x) - 1.$$

This can be written as a quadratic equation $x[H(x)]^2 - H(x) + 1 = 0$ in $H(x)$ and solved to obtain

$$H(x) = \frac{1 \pm \sqrt{1 - 4x}}{2x}.$$

The final task is to decide which of these solutions to take as the generating function. This can be done by considering the behaviour of these functions in the neighbourhood of $x = 0$. Note that

$$\frac{1 + \sqrt{1 - 4x}}{2x} \rightarrow \infty$$

as x approaches 0 from above.

Then, since $H(0) = C_0 = 1$, it can be seen that

$$H(x) = \frac{1 - \sqrt{1 - 4x}}{2x}. \qquad \qquad \square$$

Expanding $H(x)$ as a power series allows us to obtain a formula for C_n, as follows:

$$
\begin{aligned}
H(x) &= \frac{1}{2x}\left(1 - \sqrt{1 - 4x}\right) \\
&= \frac{1}{2x}\left(1 - \left[1 + \frac{\left(\frac{1}{2}\right)}{1!}(-4x) + \frac{\left(\frac{1}{2}\right)\left(-\frac{1}{2}\right)}{2!}(-4x)^2 \right.\right. \\
&\qquad\qquad\qquad\left.\left. + \frac{\left(\frac{1}{2}\right)\left(-\frac{1}{2}\right)\left(-\frac{3}{2}\right)}{3!}(-4x)^3 + \cdots\right]\right) \\
&= \frac{1}{4x}\left(\frac{1}{1!}(4x) + \frac{\left(\frac{1}{2}\right)}{2!}(4x)^2 + \frac{\left(\frac{1}{2}\right)\left(\frac{3}{2}\right)}{3!}(4x)^3 + \cdots \right. \\
&\qquad\qquad\left. + \frac{\left(\frac{1}{2}\right)\left(\frac{3}{2}\right)\cdots\left(\frac{2n-1}{2}\right)}{(n+1)!}(4x)^{n+1} + \cdots\right) \\
&= 1 + x + 2x^2 + \cdots + \frac{4^n \times 1 \times 3 \times 5 \times \cdots \times (2n-1)}{2^n(n+1)!}x^n + \cdots
\end{aligned}
$$

Thus

$$
\begin{aligned}
C_n &= \frac{1}{n+1} \times \frac{2^n \times 1 \times 3 \times 5 \times \cdots \times (2n-1)}{n!} \\
&= \frac{1}{n+1} \times \frac{2^n \times 1 \times 3 \times 5 \times \cdots \times (2n-1)}{n!} \times \frac{n!}{n!} \\
&= \frac{1}{n+1} \times \frac{(2n)!}{(n!)^2} \\
&= \frac{1}{n+1} \binom{2n}{n},
\end{aligned}
\tag{7.2}
$$

which shows the simple relationship between the Catalan numbers and the central binomial coefficients (if you are a little puzzled by how we get from the second to the third line in obtaining (7.2) then you might find it helpful to look back at some of the working towards the end of the proof of Result 5.1 on page 39).

In contrast to the above algebraic methods of proving the formula for the Catalan numbers, we now give a well-known proof based on *André's reflection principle*. This principle is named after Désiré André, a 19th century French mathematician who was a student of Joseph Bertrand (whom we will meet in a later chapter). The method of proof utilises the combinatorial interpretation of C_n as the number of paths across an $n \times n$ grid which do not dip below the diagonal (refer back to Figure 7.4 for an example of such a path). Its visual nature makes it a particularly appealing proof.

ALTERNATIVE PROOF OF (7.2) Let us say that the bottom left-hand and top right-hand corners of the $n \times n$ grid have Cartesian coordinates $(0,0)$ and (n, n) respectively so that the diagonal has the Cartesian equation $y = x$. Any path that touches the diagonal at some point between $(0,0)$ and (n, n) we shall call a *t.d.*-path. Let us now consider *t.d.*-paths that go through both $(0, 1)$ and $(n-1, n)$. For any such path it is actually possible, via the judicious reflection of sections of it in the line $y = x$, to obtain a path that goes through $(1, 0)$ and $(n-1, n)$. An example of this is demonstrated in Figures 7.5 and 7.6, where $n = 5$. The path in Figure 7.5 is a *t.d.*-path going through $(0, 1)$ and $(4, 5)$. In Figure 7.6 part of this path has been reflected in $y = x$ so that the resultant path goes through $(1, 0)$ and $(4, 5)$.

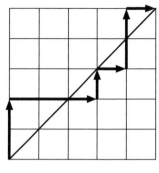

Figure 7.5

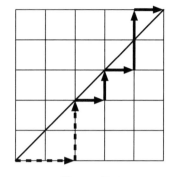

Figure 7.6

Task 7.2   Convince yourself, via the above reflection procedure, that there is a one-to-one correspondence between *t.d.*-paths that go through both $(0,1)$ and $(n-1,n)$ and all paths that go through both $(1,0)$ and $(n-1,n)$.

The total number of paths going through $(1,0)$ and $(n-1,n)$ is

$$^{(n-2)+n}C_{n-2} = \,^{2(n-1)}C_{n-2}.$$

From the result of Task 7.2 it can be seen that this also the number of *t.d.*-paths from $(0,1)$ to $(n-1,n)$. There are $^{2(n-1)}C_{n-1}$ paths from $(0,1)$ to $(n-1,n)$, so that the number of paths between these points that are not *t.d.*-paths is

$$
\begin{aligned}
\binom{2(n-1)}{n-1} - \binom{2(n-1)}{n-2} &= \frac{[2(n-1)]!}{(n-1)!(n-1)!} - \frac{[2(n-1)]!}{n!(n-2)!} \\
&= \frac{[2(n-1)]!}{(n-1)!(n-1)!}\left(1 - \frac{n-1}{n}\right) \\
&= \frac{1}{n}\binom{2(n-1)}{n-1}.
\end{aligned}
$$

Now note that the paths from $(0,1)$ to $(n-1,n)$ that are not *t.d.*-paths are precisely those paths from that do not dip below the diagonal of the $(n-1) \times (n-1)$ grid with corners situated at $(0,1)$, $(0,n)$, $(n-1,n)$ and $(n-1,1)$. This shows that

$$C_n = \frac{1}{n+1}\binom{2n}{n}.$$

❑

The Catalan numbers are named after the Belgian mathematician, Eugène Charles Catalan (1814-1894). Their combinatorial interpretations guarantee that each member of the sequence $\{C_n\}$ is actually an integer, although, on looking at the nth term above, this would not appear to be an obvious fact. You are asked to consider this further in Exercise 7.

Challenge 7.1   Use Result 5.3 to obtain the asymptotic relation

$$C_n \sim \frac{2^{2n}}{\sqrt{n^3 \pi}}.$$

Notes

(i) Some textbooks define the nth Catalan number by

$$C_n = \frac{1}{n}\binom{2(n-1)}{n-1},$$

in which case their nth term gives our $(n-1)$th term.

(ii) You can find an inductive proof of the formula for the Catalan numbers in [11].

Exercise 7

1. Use (1.6) to prove that $n+1$ divides $2^n C_n$ for all non-negative integers n.

2. (a) Show that the Catalan numbers satisfy the recurrence relation

$$C_n = \frac{2(2n-1)}{n+1} C_{n-1}.$$

   (b) Given that $C_5 = 42$, use the above recurrence relation to work out C_6, C_7 and C_8.

3. A regular n-sided polygon can, by drawing in $n - 3$ non-intersecting diagonals, be split up into $n - 2$ triangles in approximately 4×10^{51} ways. By using Challenge 7.1, or otherwise, find n.

4. Calculate C_1, C_3, C_7 and C_{15}, and record your answers. Then work out C_n for several other values of n. Use your results to make a conjecture about C_n when $n = 2^k - 1$ and when $n \neq 2^k - 1$.

5. Consider the voting scenario interpretation of the Catalan numbers. Of the C_n allowed voting patterns on $2n$ votes let A_n be, for $n \geq 2$, the number of them in which candidate a receives the first 2 votes. Prove that $A_n > \frac{1}{2} C_n$ when $n \geq 3$.

Chapter 8

Random processes and $^{2n}C_n$

The central binomial coefficients often crop up in problems associated with probability and random processes. In this chapter we look at two particular examples, both of which can be associated with simple experiments involving the tossing of a fair coin. It is first shown how the numbers $^{2n}C_n$ can arise in calculations concerning a process called a 'random walk'. In particular, something really rather interesting will be proved about the length of time it takes on average to get back to the starting point. Second, we consider the random process whereby a coin is flipped continually until at least n heads and n tails have appeared, with the aim of calculating the expected number of tosses required to achieve this.

Let us pose the first problem. Imagine tossing a fair coin and keeping a tally of the number of heads and tails that appear. Before any tosses have been made the number of heads and tails will both be zero. How many tosses, on average, will you have to make before the number of heads and tails obtained are equal once more? When the answer to this question is finally revealed you might initially find it somewhat surprising.

A sequence of heads and tails can be thought of as a random walk in one dimension, and can be represented by a 'zig-zag' graph. For example, the sequence HHHTTHTTTTH can be represented as shown in Figure 8.1 on the following page. The variable y on the vertical axis represents the number of heads obtained to that point minus the number of tails obtained to that point. Note that although Figure 8.1 might give the impression that the random walk is in two dimensions, we need to remember that

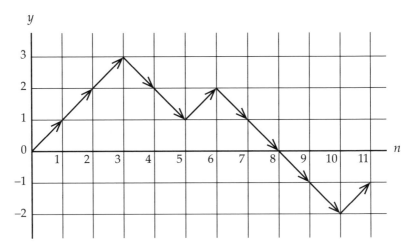

Figure 8.1: A coin-tossing sequence as a random walk

the horizontal axis is merely used to keep track of the order in which the heads and tails occur (it can be thought of as a time-axis).

Let N be the random variable representing the number of tosses made up to and including the first toss that results in the number of heads and tails being equal. Then $P(N = 2n)$ denotes the probability that after the $(2n)$th toss of the coin there are n heads and n tails, but at no point before then were the number of heads and tails equal. We first find an expression for $P(N = 2n)$ where n is a positive integer, noting that $P(N = 2n - 1) = 0$.

Suppose that $N = 2n$, so that $y(2n) = 0$. If the first toss resulted in a head, so that $y(1) = 1$, then the path on our diagram must be such that $y(2n - 1) = 1$. It is in fact the case that the number of possible sequences of heads and tails from the second to the $(2n - 1)$th toss inclusive, given that $N = 2n$, is equal to the $(n - 1)$th Catalan number, C_{n-1}. To see this we may note that this number is equal to the number of sequences of Hs and Ts of length $2n - 2$ such that there are $n - 1$ heads and $n - 1$ tails, and where the number of Hs to any point in this sequence is always at least as large as the number of tails to that point (the result then follows, remembering the combinatorial interpretations of the Catalan numbers given in Chapter 7). Then, in order for y to be equal to 0 after the $(2n)$th toss there must have been a tail on the $(2n)$th toss. A similar situation would arise if the first toss resulted in a tail. Thus, noting that there are $2^{2(n-1)}$ possible sequences from the second to the $(2n-1)$th toss inclusive, it follows that

$$
\begin{aligned}
P(N = 2n) &= \frac{C_{n-1}}{2^{2(n-1)}} \times P(\text{T on } (2n)\text{th toss}) \\
&= \frac{C_{n-1}}{2^{2(n-1)}} \times \tfrac{1}{2} \\
&= \frac{1}{2^{2n-1}} \times \frac{1}{(n-1)+1} \binom{2(n-1)}{n-1} \\
&= \frac{1}{2^{2n-1}} \times \frac{1}{n} \times \frac{[2(n-1)]!}{(n-1)!(n-1)!} \\
&= \frac{1}{2^{2n-1}} \times \frac{1}{n} \times \frac{n^2}{2n(2n-1)} \times \frac{(2n)!}{n!n!} \\
&= \frac{1}{2^{2n}(2n-1)} \binom{2n}{n}.
\end{aligned}
\tag{8.1}
$$

For a specific example of this, refer to Figure 8.1 for which $N = 8$. It can be seen that the first toss resulted in a head. From the second to the seventh toss inclusive there are 2^6 possible paths, of which C_3 contain exactly three heads and three tails such that the number of heads at each point is not exceeded by the number of tails up to that point (the one shown being HHTTHT). The eighth toss then resulted in a tail to give $N = 8$.

We now go on to calculate $E(N)$, the expectation of N. This is the average number of tosses of a fair coin required up to the first point at which an equal number of heads and tails have been obtained. It is given by

$$
E(N) = \sum_{k=1}^{\infty} 2k\, P(N = 2k),
$$

and — now for the surprise! — the series diverges so that $E(N)$ is infinite. To see this, note that (8.1) gives

$$
2k\, P(N = 2k) = \frac{2k}{2^{2k}(2k-1)} \binom{2k}{k} > \frac{1}{4^k} \binom{2k}{k}.
$$

We now scent trouble because

$$
\sum_{k=1}^{\infty} \frac{1}{4^k} \binom{2k}{k}
$$

corresponds to trying to put the boundary value $x = \tfrac{1}{4}$ into the series (6.2). To translate this into a watertight argument we demonstrate that, given any (large) 'target sum' T, a value of m can be found such that

$$\sum_{k=1}^{m} 2k\, P(N = 2k) > T.$$

To do this, use (6.2) to choose some fixed value of x, x_0 say, with x_0 just less than $\frac{1}{4}$ so that

$$\frac{1}{\sqrt{1 - 4x_0}} > T.$$

Then, since the sum in (6.2) converges to

$$\frac{1}{\sqrt{1 - 4x_0}},$$

it follows that, for all sufficiently large m,

$$T < \sum_{k=1}^{m} x_0^k \binom{2k}{k} < \sum_{k=1}^{m} \frac{1}{4^k} \binom{2k}{k} < \sum_{k=1}^{m} 2k\, P(N = 2k) < E(N).$$

The above tells us that $E(N)$ does not actually exist (a fact that we denote by $E(N) = \infty$). This (possibly counter-intuitive) result contrasts with the finite expectations of some other discrete random variables taking infinitely many values that you may already have met. For example, the geometric random variable (taking values $1, 2, 3, \ldots$) with parameter p has expectation $\frac{1}{p}$ and the Poisson random variable (taking values $0, 1, 2, \ldots$) with parameter m has expectation m.

Now consider a slightly different coin-tossing scenario in which our numbers ${}^{2n}C_n$ also appear. This time we continue flipping a fair coin up to the first point at which at least n heads and n tails have come up. Let X_n be the random variable representing the number of tosses required to achieve at least n heads and n tails. Our aim here is to calculate $E(X_n)$.

Note first that $P(X_n = k) = 0$ when $k < 2n$, so that the sum for $E(X_n)$ can be started from $k = 2n$. Let us suppose that the first point at which at least n heads and n tails have come up occurs on the kth toss. Then there will have been either exactly $n - 1$ heads or exactly $n - 1$ tails in the first $k - 1$ tosses of the coin. In the former case the kth toss must have resulted in a head while in the latter case it must have been a tail. The number of sequences of $k - 1$ tosses in which exactly $n - 1$ heads have occurred is ${}^{k-1}C_{n-1}$, and the same is true for the number of sequences of $k - 1$ tosses in which exactly $n - 1$ tails have appeared. Finally, noting that there are 2^{k-1} possible outcomes when a coin is tossed $k - 1$ times, we obtain

$$P(X_n = k) = P(X_n = k \mid k\text{th toss a head}) + P(X_n = k \mid k\text{th toss a tail})$$

$$= \frac{1}{2^{k-1}} \binom{k-1}{n-1} \times \tfrac{1}{2} + \frac{1}{2^{k-1}} \binom{k-1}{n-1} \times \tfrac{1}{2}$$

$$= \frac{1}{2^{k-1}} \binom{k-1}{n-1}$$

From an intuitive point of view we would certainly expect to obtain at least n heads and n tails if we toss the coin for long enough, something that may be expressed more formally as

$$\sum_{k=2n}^{m} P(X_n = k) \to 1 \text{ as } m \to \infty$$

Assuming this to be true, we have a probabilistic proof of the result

$$\sum_{k=2n}^{\infty} \frac{1}{2^{k-1}} \binom{k-1}{n-1} = 1 \tag{8.2}$$

Challenge 8.1 You may feel that our argument used to obtain (8.2) was not entirely watertight. As we shall be using this result in due course, you might want have a go at proving it without using probabilistic arguments.

It now follows that

$$E(X_n) = \sum_{k=1}^{\infty} k\, P(X_n = k)$$

$$= \sum_{k=2n}^{\infty} \frac{k(k-1)!}{2^{k-1}(n-1)!(k-n)!}$$

$$= \sum_{k=2n}^{\infty} \frac{n}{2^{k-1}} \binom{k}{n}$$

$$= 2n \sum_{k=2n}^{\infty} \frac{1}{2^k} \binom{k}{n}. \tag{8.3}$$

In order to make further progress we rewrite (8.3) as

$$E(X_n) = 2n \sum_{k=2n+1}^{\infty} \frac{1}{2^{k-1}} \binom{k-1}{n}$$

$$= 2n \left[\sum_{k=2(n+1)}^{\infty} \frac{1}{2^{k-1}} \binom{k-1}{n} + \frac{1}{2^{(2n+1)-1}} \binom{(2n+1)-1}{n} \right].$$

Note that the infinite sum in the brackets above is just the left-hand side of (8.2) with $n-1$ replaced with n. Thus

$$E(X_n) = 2n \left[1 + \frac{1}{2^{2n}} \binom{2n}{n} \right].$$

Using this with Result 5.3 gives

$$E(X_n) \sim 2n \left[1 + \frac{1}{\sqrt{n\pi}} \right]. \tag{8.4}$$

The first, if rather obvious, thing to note is that, in contrast to the previous example, the expectation is finite. It is also instructive to interpret (8.4) from an intuitive point of view. Since the minimum number of tosses required to obtain at least n heads and n tails is $2n$, we may regard any flips that are needed beyond this number as 'excess' tosses. From

$$E(X_n) - 2n \sim 2n \left[1 + \frac{1}{\sqrt{n\pi}} \right] - 2n = 2\sqrt{\frac{n}{\pi}}$$

it follows that the expected number of excess tosses increases without limit as n increases, roughly in proportion to $\sqrt{n}$. However, the fact that

$$\frac{E(X_n)}{2n} \sim 1 + \frac{1}{\sqrt{n\pi}}$$

tells us that the ratio of the number of excess tosses required to the total number of tosses required tends to 0 as n increases without limit. We feel that both these properties of $E(X_n)$ are what might be expected intuitively.

The above problem is also tackled in [6] using recurrence arguments as opposed to the series methods employed here. There the variance of X_n is also calculated.

Challenge 8.2   This is a question that has been adapted from one given in [2]. Imagine that you are standing right at the very edge of a swimming pool, and are holding a bag containing n blue and n red balls. You draw the balls out one at a time, without replacement. If you take out a blue ball you take one step back, but if the ball is red you take one step forward (assume that all your steps are of the same size). You continue with this until either you end up in the pool or all the balls have been drawn out of the bag.

Show, by relating this problem to the central binomial coefficients and Catalan numbers, that the probability that you remain dry is $\frac{1}{n+1}$.

Exercise 8

1. You toss a fair coin 10 times. What is the probability that

   (a) You get 5 heads and 5 tails?

   (b) You get 5 heads and 5 tails but the running totals of heads and tails are never equal until the final toss?

2. Approximately how many times on average will you have to flip a fair coin in order to obtain at least 1 million heads and 1 million tails?

3. A fair cubical die with 1 to 6 on its faces is rolled $2n$ times.

   (a) Find an expression for the probability that exactly half of the rolls resulted in a 6.

   (b) What is the smallest value of n such that there is less than a one in a million chance of getting exactly n sixes?

4. You roll a fair cubical die and record the number that comes up, k say. You then toss a fair coin $2k$ times. What is the probability that you get an equal number of heads and tails?

5. Consider a generalisation of the previous question, whereby instead of rolling a die you roll a fair n-sided spinner with its edges numbered from 1 to n. If k comes up on the spinner you toss a fair coin $2k$ times. Show that the probability of obtaining an equal number of heads and tails is given by the expression

$$\frac{1}{n} \left[\frac{2n+1}{2^{2n}} \binom{2n}{n} - 1 \right].$$

6. Show that

$$\mathrm{Var}(X_n) = 2n \left[1 + \frac{1}{2^{2n}} \binom{2n}{n} \right] - \left[\frac{n}{2^{2n-1}} \binom{2n}{n} \right]^2,$$

where X_n is the random variable representing the number of tosses of a fair coin required to achieve at least n heads and n tails.

Chapter 9

Comparing coefficients

In this chapter we demonstrate a mathematical technique that allows us to prove a variety of numerical results concerning certain types of sums. In keeping with the theme of this book, we shall concentrate on sums that are related in some way to $^{2n}C_n$. However, the methods presented here certainly have more general applicability.

Let $f(x)$ and $g(x)$ be two non-zero polynomials of degree m and n respectively. Then we can write

$$f(x) = a_m x^m + a_{m-1} x^{m-1} + \cdots + a_0$$
$$\text{and} \quad g(x) = b_n x^n + b_{n-1} x^{n-1} + \cdots + b_0$$

where $a_m \neq 0$ and $b_n \neq 0$. For the situation where $m = n$ and $a_k = b_k$, $k = 0, 1, 2, \ldots, m$, it is obvious that $f(x) = g(x)$ for all real values of x. Is the converse true? In other words, if $f(x) = g(x)$ for all values of x, then is it true that $m = n$ and $a_k = b_k$, $k = 0, 1, 2, \ldots, m$? If we suppose that the converse is not true then $f(x)$ and $g(x)$ differ in at least one coefficient of x so that $f(x) - g(x)$ is some non-zero polynomial, $h(x)$ say. However, the assumption $f(x) = g(x)$ for all values of x means that $h(x) = 0$ for all values of x, providing us with a contradiction since only the zero polynomial is equal to 0 for all x.

Therefore $f(x) = g(x)$ for all real values of x if, and only if, $f(x)$ and $g(x)$ are exactly the same as polynomials. If $f(x) = g(x)$ for all x then $f(x)$ and $g(x)$ are said to be *identical* as polynomials, a fact denoted by $f(x) \equiv g(x)$. With care, this idea can be extended to power series.

Here is a simple example to illustrate the key ideas involved in 'comparing coefficients'. If $f(x) = (1+x)^2(1+x)^5$ and $g(x) = (1+x)^7$ then $f(x) \equiv g(x)$. We know in particular that when each of these functions is expanded and subsequently expressed as a sum of powers of x they will possess the same coefficient of x^n for each n. So if for some integer k we obtain an expression for the coefficient of x^k in $f(x)$ and also an expression for the coefficient of x^k in $g(x)$ then these two expressions will be equal. For example, the coefficient of x^3 in $f(x)$ may be calculated as

$$\binom{2}{0}\binom{5}{3} + \binom{2}{1}\binom{5}{2} + \binom{2}{2}\binom{5}{1} \tag{9.1}$$

while that in $g(x)$ is clearly

$$\binom{7}{3}. \tag{9.2}$$

Since $f(x)$ and $g(x)$ are identical it must be the case that the numerical expressions given by (9.1) and (9.2) are equal.

This technique can be used to obtain rather more general results than that given above. For example, Result 9.1 below is proved by way of the algebraic identity $(1+x)^n(1-x)^n \equiv (1-x^2)^n$.

Result 9.1

$$\sum_{k=0}^{n} (-1)^k \binom{n}{k}^2 = \begin{cases} 0 & \text{if } n \text{ is odd,} \\ (-1)^m \dbinom{2m}{m} & \text{if } n = 2m. \end{cases}$$

PROOF The method of proof is to equate the coefficient of x^n on both sides of the identity

$$(1+x)^n(1-x)^n \equiv (1-x^2)^n.$$

Now $(1+x)^n(1-x)^n$ is equal to

$$\left[\binom{n}{0} + \binom{n}{1}x + \binom{n}{2}x^2 + \cdots + \binom{n}{n}x^n \right]$$

$$\times \left[\binom{n}{0} - \binom{n}{1}x + \binom{n}{2}x^2 - \cdots + (-1)^n \binom{n}{n}x^n \right]$$

so that the coefficient of x^n on the left-hand side of the identity is

$$(-1)^n \binom{n}{0}\binom{n}{n} + (-1)^{n-1}\binom{n}{1}\binom{n}{n-1} + (-1)^{n-2}\binom{n}{2}\binom{n}{n-2}$$
$$+ \cdots + (-1)^0 \binom{n}{n}\binom{n}{0} = \sum_{k=0}^{n}(-1)^k \binom{n}{k}^2,$$

using the symmetry property (1.1).

Next consider the right-hand side of the identity. It is clear that, for any integer k, the coefficient of x^k in $(1 - x^2)^n$ is zero if k is odd. Thus in particular it is the case that the coefficient of x^n in $(1 - x^2)^n$ is zero when n is odd. On the other hand, if $n = 2m$ then the coefficient of x^n in $(1 - x^2)^n$ is given by

$$(-1)^m \binom{2m}{m}.$$

❏

We have already used a combinatorial argument to prove Result 2.2:

$$\sum_{k=0}^{n}\binom{n}{k}^2 = \binom{2n}{n}.$$

Now, after having gone through the proof of Result 9.1, you will probably find it all rather obvious that Result 2.2 can also be obtained by comparing coefficients on both sides of the identity $(1 + x)^n (1 + x)^n \equiv (1 + x)^{2n}$.

As an exercise in Chapter 2 you were asked to construct a combinatorial argument to prove that

$$\sum_{k=0}^{n-1}\binom{n-1}{k}\binom{n+1}{k+1} = \binom{2n}{n} \quad \text{for } n \geq 1.$$

It is possible to obtain a more general version of this result by comparing coefficients:

Result 9.2

$$\sum_{k=0}^{n-m}\binom{n-m}{k}\binom{n+m}{k+m} = \binom{2n}{n} \quad \text{for } n \geq m.$$

PROOF In order to prove this result we equate the coefficient of x^n on both sides of the identity

$$(1 + x)^{n-m}(1 + x)^{n+m} \equiv (1 + x)^{2n}$$

to obtain

$$\binom{n-m}{0}\binom{n+m}{n} + \binom{n-m}{1}\binom{n+m}{n-1}$$
$$+ \cdots + \binom{n-m}{n-m}\binom{n+m}{m} = \binom{2n}{n}.$$

To get the stated result it is now just a matter of using the symmetry property (1.1) of the binomial coefficients. ❑

Challenge 9.1   Here is yet another interesting property of the sequence $\{^{2n}C_n\}$. The first few terms of the sequence are listed below for convenience:

$$1,\ 2,\ 6,\ 20,\ 70,\ 252,\ 924,\ 3\,432,\ 12\,870, \ldots .$$

Consider the following calculations using these terms:

$$1 \times 1 = 1,$$
$$1 \times 2 + 2 \times 1 = 4,$$
$$1 \times 6 + 2 \times 2 + 6 \times 1 = 16,$$
$$1 \times 20 + 2 \times 6 + 6 \times 2 + 20 \times 1 = 64,$$
$$1 \times 70 + 2 \times 20 + 6 \times 6 + 20 \times 2 + 70 \times 1 = 256,$$

and so on. The nth calculation would be

$$^0C_0 \times {}^{2(n-1)}C_{n-1} + {}^2C_1 \times {}^{2(n-2)}C_{n-2} + \cdots + {}^{2(n-1)}C_{n-1} \times {}^0C_0.$$

From the above results it might be conjectured that the nth answer is always 4^{n-1}. Show that this is in fact true by using (6.2).

Exercise 9

1. (a) By considering the identity

$$(1+x)^m(1+x)^n \equiv (1+x)^{m+n},$$

obtain a generalisation of the equality between the numerical expressions given by (9.1) and (9.2).

(b) Hence obtain a quick evaluation of

$$\binom{9}{0}\binom{17}{11} + \binom{9}{1}\binom{17}{10} + \binom{9}{2}\binom{17}{9} + \cdots + \binom{9}{9}\binom{17}{2}.$$

2. Give a combinatorial proof of your generalised result from the previous question.

3. Use the method of comparing coefficients to prove that

$$\sum_{i+j+k=n} \binom{n}{i}\binom{n}{j}\binom{n}{k} = \binom{3n}{n}.$$

4. (a) Show that

$$(1+x)^{2n} + (1-x)^{2n} = 2\sum_{k=0}^{n}\binom{2n}{2k}x^{2k}.$$

(b) Find the coefficient of x^{2n} in $\left[(1+x)^{2n} + (1-x)^{2n}\right]^2$.

(c) Hence obtain the result

$$\sum_{k=0}^{n}\binom{2n}{2k}^2 = \tfrac{1}{2}\left[\binom{4n}{2n} + (-1)^n\binom{2n}{n}\right].$$

5. Show that

$$\sum_{k=0}^{n-1}\binom{2n}{2k+1}^2$$

can be expressed in terms of a simple formula involving two central binomial coefficients.

Chapter 10

Extending the definition of $^{2n}C_n$

Since $^{2n}C_n$ was introduced via the idea of counting the number of possible selections of n students from $2n$ students it is only natural that we have thus far simply defined it on the non-negative whole numbers n. The 'graph' of $^{2n}C_n$ can therefore be thought of as a series of points at $(1, 2)$, $(2, 6)$, $(3, 20)$, and so on. A pertinent question that might be asked at this stage is "Can we define a smooth, continuous function that joins up these points?". You may already have anticipated the answer to this, having spotted that in one of the previous chapters lurked the opportunity to extend the definition of $^{2n}C_n$ to all positive real numbers t. In Challenge 5.1 $^{2n}C_n$ was expressed in terms of an improper integral:

$$\binom{2n}{n} = \frac{2^{2n+1}}{\pi} \int_0^\infty \frac{1}{(x^2+1)^{n+1}} \, dx.$$

Now the above integral is actually defined for any $n \geq 0$, not just when n is an integer. So we may then define $^{2t}C_t$ as

$$\frac{2^{2t+1}}{\pi} \int_0^\infty \frac{1}{(x^2+1)^{t+1}} \, dx, \ t \geq 0. \tag{10.1}$$

This is a continuous function on the non-negative real numbers that agrees with $^{2n}C_n$ on the non-negative integers, the graph of which is shown in Figure 10.1 for $1 \leq t \leq 5$ (notice its smooth, exponential-type behaviour).

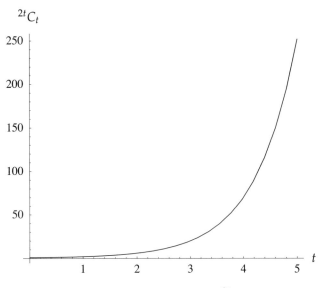

Figure 10.1: The graph of $^{2t}C_t$

The generalised function $^{2t}C_t$ can also be expressed in terms of a special function called the *gamma function*. This is denoted by $\Gamma(t)$ and defined for all real $t > 0$ via an integral as follows:

$$\Gamma(t) = \int_0^\infty x^{t-1} e^{-x} \, dx.$$

Integrating by parts gives

$$\begin{aligned}
\Gamma(t) &= \left[-x^{t-1} e^{-x} \right]_0^\infty - \int_0^\infty (t-1) x^{t-2} (-e^{-x}) \, dx \\
&= (t-1) \int_0^\infty x^{(t-1)-1} e^{-x} \, dx \\
&= (t-1)\Gamma(t-1).
\end{aligned} \tag{10.2}$$

Note also that

$$\Gamma(1) = \int_0^\infty e^{-x} \, dx = 1. \tag{10.3}$$

We can use (10.2) and (10.3) to obtain an expression for $\Gamma(n)$, where n is a positive integer with $n \geq 2$, as follows:

$$\begin{aligned}
\Gamma(n) &= (n-1)\Gamma(n-1) \\
&= (n-1)(n-2)\Gamma(n-2) \\
&= (n-1(n-2)(n-3)\Gamma(n-3) \\
&\qquad\vdots \\
&= (n-1(n-2)(n-3)\ldots\Gamma(1) \\
&= (n-1)!.
\end{aligned}$$

Thus the gamma function can be thought of as a generalisation, to the real numbers, of the factorial function. It is one of those functions that frequently crop up in advanced mathematics.

Since

$$\binom{2n}{n} = \frac{(2n)!}{(n!)^2} = \frac{\Gamma(2n+1)}{[\Gamma(n+1)]^2},$$

we can use $^{2t}C_t = \frac{\Gamma(2t+1)}{[\Gamma(t+1)]^2}$ as a generalisation of $^{2n}C_n$ to all real $n > 0$. A graph of the gamma function for $0 < t \leq 6$ is given in Figure 10.2.

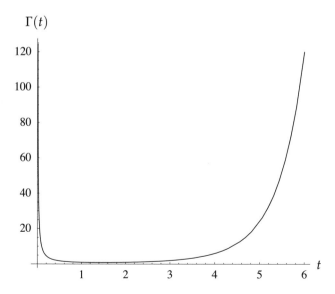

Figure 10.2: The graph of $\Gamma(t)$

Research Activity 10.1   There are many interesting results involving the gamma function. Here are just two of them:

(a) $\Gamma(x)\Gamma(1-x) = \dfrac{\pi}{\sin \pi x}$ for $0 < x < 1$.

(b) $\Gamma\left(\frac{1}{2}\right) = \sqrt{\pi}$.

Find out as much about the gamma function as you can, and have a go at proving some of the results associated with them. We may even extend the definition of the gamma function to all complex numbers except for $0, -1, -2, -3, \ldots$. This process is called *analytic continuation* and is covered in university courses in complex analysis.

Challenge 10.1   Show that when n is a non-negative integer:

$$\int_0^1 [x(1-x)]^n \, dx = \frac{1}{2^n C_n (2n+1)}.$$

Research Activity 10.2   The above integral evaluates special cases of a well-known mathematical function called the *beta function*. Look up the general version of this function and find out its relationship to the gamma function and the central binomial coefficients.

Challenge 10.2   See if you can find a way to prove that

$$\pi = \sum_{k=0}^{\infty} \frac{2^{k+1}}{2^k C_k (2k+1)}.$$

Knowledge of the beta function might of use here.

Exercise 10

1. What happens when we attempt to use the integral (10.1) to extend the definition of $^{2n}C_n$ to the negative integers?

2. Use (10.2), along with the result $\Gamma\left(\frac{1}{2}\right) = \sqrt{\pi}$, to obtain an exact numerical expression for $\Gamma\left(\frac{7}{2}\right)$.

3. (a) Use (10.1) to find an exact numerical expression for $\binom{1}{\frac{1}{2}}$.

   (b) Let n be a non-negative integer. Show that

   $$\binom{2n+1}{\frac{2n+1}{2}} = \frac{2^{4n+2}}{\pi(2n+1)\ ^{2n}C_n}.$$

4. The integral

   $$\int_0^1 x^{n-1}(1-x)^n\,dx$$

   evaluates particular cases of the beta function. By using this integral, or otherwise, show that

   $$\sum_{k=0}^{n} \frac{(-1)^k}{n+k}\binom{n}{k} = \frac{1}{n\ ^{2n}C_n}.$$

Chapter 11

More on the Catalan numbers

Another well-known combinatorial interpretation of the Catalan numbers is in connection with *binary trees*, which are special types of *graphs*. The usage of the term 'graph' here is quite different from the sense in the phrase 'the graph of $y = x^3 - 4x$', for example. We are talking about the types of graphs consisting of nodes and arcs, used to represent networks such as towns and the roads connecting them. If you would like to learn a little more about the mathematics associated with the types of graphs being considered here then [5] might be a good start. In connection with graphs, 'tree structure' implies some sort of branching relationship between the nodes of a graph, a bit like that found in the trees of nature. A binary tree with n nodes is a graph with a hierarchical structure, having the following properties and recursive definition:

(a) There is one node that is designated as the *root*, that can be considered to be at the top (or bottom) of the structure. This has either one or two arcs emanating from it (unless $n = 1$, in which case the graph will consist of the root alone).

(b) The remaining $n - 1$ nodes are partitioned into two disjoint sets such that each of these is in turn a tree (called the left and right *subtrees* of the root).

(c) A binary tree is always connected.

(d) The graph contains no cycles.

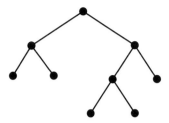

Figure 11.1: A binary tree with nine nodes

When drawing binary trees it seems conventional to put the root at the top of the tree! Figure 11.1 shows an example of a binary tree with nine nodes (and automatically, therefore, eight arcs). Note that the binary trees on two vertices given by

are considered to be distinct as binary trees. In other words, there is a distinction between left and right in these structures. The Catalan numbers do in fact enumerate the number of distinct binary trees on n nodes. As mentioned previously, for $n = 1$ there is only one binary tree, that consisting of a single node. There are only two possible binary trees for $n = 2$, those depicted above. Figure 11.2 gives the five possible binary trees for $n = 3$.

Figure 11.2: The five possible binary trees for $n = 3$

Task 11.1   Draw out all possible binary trees for $n = 4$ (there should be fourteen of them).

Challenge 11.1   Try to prove that C_n gives the number of distinct binary trees on n nodes.

There would also appear to be a simple way of obtaining the Catalan numbers from Pascal's triangle. Remembering that the topmost row is called the zeroth row and the leftmost entries are called the zeroth elements of their rows, notice that we obtain

$$2 - 1 = 2, \ 6 - 4 = 2, \ 20 - 15 = 5, \text{ and } 70 - 56 = 14,$$

on calculating the difference between certain consecutive elements from the second, fourth, sixth and eighth rows respectively. For ease of reference Pascal's triangle is reproduced again in Table 11.1.

Row

0					1					
1				1		1				
2			1		2		1			
3		1		3		3		1		
4		1	4		6		4		1	
5	1		5	10		10		5		1
6	1	6		15	20		15	6		1
7	1	7	21		35	35		21	7	1
8	1	8	28	56		70	56	28	8	1

Table 11.1: Pascal's triangle

Challenge 11.2 Make a conjecture relating the Catalan numbers to the difference between certain consecutive entries in Pascal's triangle. Extend the triangle by a few more rows to see if this pattern does in fact continue any further, and, if it does, try to prove that your conjecture is actually true.

Yet another combinatorial interpretation of these numbers is connected to the way that we can use brackets to evaluate a sum of n terms. The brackets are positioned so that the sum is evaluated by performing one addition at a time. Let us first consider the sum $x + y + z$. There are the following two ways of evaluating this sum:

$$((x + y) + z) \text{ or } (x + (y + z)).$$

In the first of these x is added to y and then the result is added to z, while in the second y is added to z and the result is added to x. The above expressions are, in [2], termed *bracketed expressions* and we adopt the same phrase here. What about the evaluation of $w + x + y + z$? This is the subject of the next task.

Task 11.2   Two possible bracketed expressions of four terms are $(((w + x) + y) + z)$ and $(w + ((x + y) + z))$. List the remaining three possibilities.

If this bracketing process does indeed give the Catalan numbers then the above results would imply that C_n gives the number of bracketed expressions of $n + 1$ terms. Let us prove that this is the case:

Result 11.1 *The number of bracketed expressions of $n + 1$ terms is given by C_n.*

PROOF Let B_n be the number of ways of bracketing n terms where $n \geq 2$, with $B_1 = 1$ by definition. Consider what happens when the outermost pair of brackets is removed from some bracketed expression of n terms. If $n = 2$ then we are left with just two individual terms. On the other hand, if $n \geq 3$ then we end up either with two sets of bracketed expressions or a single term and a bracketed expression. The diagram below depicts the former of these scenarios:

$((m \text{ terms}) + (n - m \text{ terms}))$ $\longrightarrow$ $(m \text{ terms}) + (n - m \text{ terms})$

one bracketed expression of n terms   remove   two bracketed expresssions
                                         outermost
                                         brackets

Summing from $m = 1$ to $m = n - 1$ then gives

$$\begin{aligned} B_n &= B_{n-1} + B_2 B_{n-2} + B_3 B_{n-3} + \cdots + B_{n-2} B_2 + B_{n-1} \\ &= B_1 B_{n-1} + B_2 B_{n-2} + B_3 B_{n-3} + \cdots + B_{n-2} B_2 + B_{n-1} B_1 \\ &= \sum_{k=1}^{n-1} B_k B_{n-k} \end{aligned}$$

The above result in conjunction with the initial condition $C_0 = B_1 = 1$ and the Catalan recurrence relation (7.1) implies that $C_n = B_{n+1}$, as required. ☐

If there are two combinatorial interpretations for the same sequence of numbers then it might seem reasonable to expect that there is some general way of pairing up the elements of these two enumerating sets for each n. For example, in Chapter 7 we demonstrated a one-to-one correspondence between the Catalan voting patterns and the paths going from one corner of a $n \times n$ grid to the opposite corner that do not dip below the diagonal. Thus, although the mapping might not be quite as obvious as for the case just mentioned, we would hope to be able to establish a one-to-one correspondence between the Catalan voting patterns and the bracketed expressions of $n + 1$ terms. Let us show first how this can be done when $n = 4$.

For a particular Catalan voting pattern each A is replaced with a '(' and, from left to right, each B is replaced with the next term. So, for example, the voting pattern AABABBAB would be transformed into

$$(\quad (\quad v \quad (\quad w \quad x \quad (\quad y.$$

Then the remaining term, the '+' signs and the ')'s are inserted to give a bracketed expression. You might, understandably, be worried about where to position the ')'s since it would spell disaster for our supposed one-to-one correspondence if there was more than one possibility. However, once the '('s are in position there is actually only one way of placing the four ')'s so that the bracketed expression makes mathematical sense. This is something that you should convince yourself of before moving on. For the example above, the only possibility is

$$((v + (w + x)) + (y + z)).$$

Here are two further examples (where f_4 denotes the mapping described above):

$$f_4(\text{AAAABBBB}) = ((((v + w) + x) + y) + z)$$
and $$f_4(\text{ABABAABB}) = (v + (w + ((x + y) + z))).$$

On the other hand, given any bracketed expression of five terms, this process can be reversed to obtain a unique Catalan voting pattern on eight votes. Thus not only is f_4 a function that maps each Catalan voting pattern on eight votes onto a unique bracketed expression of five terms, but it also possesses an inverse that maps each bracketed expression of five terms onto a unique Catalan voting pattern on eight votes. This establishes a one-to-one correspondence for the case $n = 4$ which can be generalised in a reasonably obvious way.

Task 11.3   Before reading any further, convince yourself, by considering some of your own examples, of the truth of the last paragraph.

To conclude this chapter we give three more situations that lead to the Catalan numbers.

First, imagine $2n$ people sitting round a circular table. The number of ways that they can shake hands in n pairs without the arm of any person crossing the arm of any other is equal to C_n.

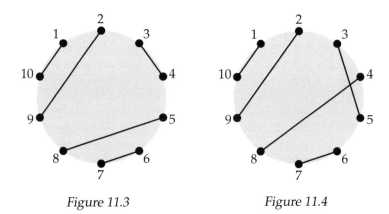

Figure 11.3   Figure 11.4

In Figures 11.3 and 11.4 the situation for $n = 5$ is considered. The 10 people sitting around the table are represented by dots and the handshakes between them by lines connecting the dots. Figure 11.3 depicts an allowed arrangement of handshakes. In Figure 11.4, however, there are two pairs whose arms cross each other, so this configuration of handshakes would not be included in the enumeration.

Challenge 11.3   Show that the above scenario does indeed generate the Catalan numbers.

Yet another way of generating the Catalan numbers is to enumerate 'mountain profiles', which are constructed subject to some simple rules which we now describe. In creating one these of one of these profiles we are allowed to use a series of diagonal upstrokes or downstrokes in such a way that we always end up at 'sea level' but never go below sea level at any stage in the construction of the landscape. Note that this means that there are necessarily n upstrokes and n downstrokes used in the creation of such an object. Figure 11.5 on the next page shows an example of a mountain profile.

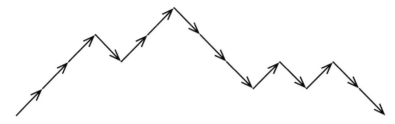

Figure 11.5: A mountain profile

It is very straightforward to show that the number of mountain profiles using n upstrokes and n downstrokes subject to the rules given above is equal to C_n. In order to do this either compare the current situation to the voting scenario discussed in detail in Chapter 7 or, even more simply, note that a profile rotated through an angle of 45 degrees corresponds to a path from the bottom left-hand corner to the top right-hand corner of an $n \times n$ grid which does not dip below the diagonal, and vice versa.

A third way of generating the Catalan numbers is by counting the number of ways that n indistinguishable balls can be placed into n distinguishable boxes such that there are never more than k balls in total in the first k boxes for each k, $k = 1, 2, \ldots, n$. Figures 11.6 and 11.7 show two different ways of distributing 4 balls amongst 4 boxes. Note that the distribution of balls shown in Figure 11.6 is allowed according to the criterion of not having more than k balls in the first k boxes while that in Figure 11.7 is not allowed since there is a total of 3 balls in the first 2 boxes. You will

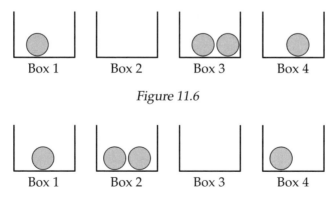

Box 1   Box 2   Box 3   Box 4

Figure 11.6

Box 1   Box 2   Box 3   Box 4

Figure 11.7

find it quite easy to establish a one-to-one correspondence between the allowed distributions of n balls amongst n boxes and the allowed voting patterns on $2n$ votes discussed in Chapter 7. This is enough to show that this 'balls in boxes' scenario does indeed enumerate the Catalan numbers.

Research Activity 11.1   See if you can find further combinatorial interpretations of the Catalan numbers. The website [15] is worth looking at if you want to find out a bit more about these numbers. The website [14] is also fun to visit for anything to do with integer sequences.

Challenge 11.4   The schematic diagram in Figure 11.8 on the facing page summarises the various interpretations of the Catalan numbers that have been considered in this book. An arrow connecting a particular pair of these interpretations indicates the fact that a one-to-one correspondence has already been established (or at least hinted at) between them.

Attempt to find a one-to-one correspondence between any pair not connected by an arrow. For example, you might try to establish a one-to-one correspondence between the binary trees on n nodes and the partitions of a regular $(n + 2)$-sided polygon into n triangles using non-intersecting diagonals of the polygon.

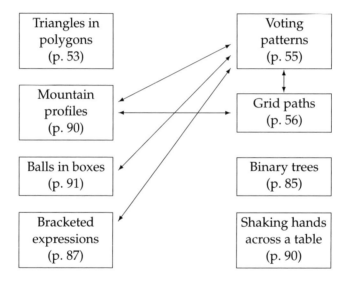

Figure 11.8

Chapter 12

Proving the same thing in different ways

Here is a list of the first sixteen Catalan numbers:

$$1, 2, 5, 14, 42, 132, 429, 1\,430, 4\,862, 16\,796, 58\,786, 208\,012, 742\,900,$$
$$2\,674\,440, 9\,694\,845, 35\,357\,670, \ldots .$$

Look at the odd terms above. Do you notice anything about their positions in the sequence? You may have spotted that they appear only to occur in the positions that are one less than a power of two (indeed, you may already have made such an observation in question 4 from Exercise 7). In other words, it might be conjectured that C_n is odd if, and only if, $n = 2^k - 1$ for some positive integer k. Here we prove only that C_n is odd if $n = 2^k - 1$ for some positive integer k, although this will be proved in two different ways. Some proofs can be far more elegant and revealing than others. You decide which of the following you prefer.

PROOF 12.1 From Result 4.1 the power of 2 in the prime factorisation of $^{2n}C_n$ is

$$\sum_{j=1}^{\infty} \left(\left\lfloor \frac{2n}{2^j} \right\rfloor - 2 \left\lfloor \frac{n}{2^j} \right\rfloor \right).$$

If $n = 2^k - 1$ then $n + 1 = 2^k$ and $C_n = {}^{2(2^k-1)}C_{2^k-1} \div 2^k$ so that the exponent of 2 in the prime factorisation of C_n is given by

$$\sum_{j=1}^{\infty} \left(\left\lfloor \frac{2(2^k-1)}{2^j} \right\rfloor - 2 \left\lfloor \frac{2^k-1}{2^j} \right\rfloor \right) - k$$

$$= \sum_{j=1}^{\infty} \left(\left\lfloor \frac{2^k-1}{2^{j-1}} \right\rfloor - 2 \left\lfloor \frac{2^k-1}{2^j} \right\rfloor \right) - k.$$

Then, on noting that

$$\left\lfloor \frac{2^k-1}{2^j} \right\rfloor = 2^{k-j} - 1 \text{ for } k \geq j,$$

it follows, using a well-known result regarding the sum of a finite geometric series, that

$$\sum_{j=1}^{\infty} \left(\left\lfloor \frac{2^k-1}{2^{j-1}} \right\rfloor - 2 \left\lfloor \frac{2^k-1}{2^j} \right\rfloor \right) - k$$

$$= \sum_{j=1}^{k} (2^j - 1) - 2 \sum_{j=1}^{k-1} (2^j - 1) - k$$

$$= (2^{k+1} - 2) - k - 2(2^k - 2) + 2(k-1) - k$$

$$= 2^{k+1} - 2 - k - 2^{k+1} + 4 + 2k - 2 - k$$

$$= 0.$$

Since the exponent of 2 in the prime factorisation of C_n is zero when $n = 2^k - 1$, C_n is necessarily odd in this case. ❑

PROOF 12.2 We proceed by induction. When $k = 1$, $2^k - 1 = 2^1 - 1 = 1$ and $C_k = C_1 = 1$, so the conjecture is true in this case. Now assume that C_{2^k-1} is odd for $k = 1, 2, \ldots, m$. The Catalan recurrence relation, obtained in Chapter 7, can be used to give

$$C_{2^{m+1}-1} = \sum_{k=1}^{2^{m+1}-1} C_{k-1} C_{n-k}$$

$$= C_0 C_{2^{m+1}-2} + \cdots + C_{2^m-1} C_{2^m-1} + \cdots + C_{2^{m+1}-2} C_0$$

$$= 2 \left(C_0 C_{2^{m+1}-2} + \cdots + C_{2^{m+1}-2} C_{2^m} \right) + C_{2^m-1} C_{2^m-1}.$$

The term C_{2^m-1} is odd by the inductive hypothesis, so that $C_{2^m-1}C_{2^m-1}$ will also be odd. The above expression for $C_{2^{m+1}-1}$ will therefore be odd, showing, by the principle of mathematical induction that C_{2^k-1} is odd for all positive integers k. ❏

Challenge 12.1   In the two proofs above it was shown only that C_{2^k-1} is odd for all positive integers k. We have not shown that all the other Catalan numbers are even. In other words, it was proved that

$$'C_n \text{ is odd if } n = 2^k - 1 \text{ for some positive integer } k'$$

rather than

$$'C_n \text{ is odd if, and only if, } n = 2^k - 1 \text{ for some positive integer } k'.$$

With a small amount of effort Proof 12.2 can be extended in order to turn it into an 'if, and only if' one. See if you can figure out how to do this.

Part II

Chapter 13

Chebyshev's bound for $\pi(x)$

The central binomial coefficients also play their part in Number Theory. In this chapter, and the next, we are going to see how $^{2n}C_n$ is used to help obtain information about the way that the prime numbers are distributed amongst the integers. The result obtained here was first proved by the Russian mathematician Pafnuty Chebyshev in 1850. The arguments presented here are based on those given in [13].

The function $\pi(x)$ represents the number of primes less than or equal to x, where x is any positive real number. For example, $\pi(18) = 7$ since there are seven primes less than or equal to 18, namely 2, 3, 5, 7, 11, 13 and 17, while $\pi(\sqrt{8}) = 1$ because 2 is the only prime less than or equal to $\sqrt{8}$. Such functions are called 'step functions', and in Figure 13.1 on the next page it can be seen why this name is so appropriate for $\pi(x)$. The graph jumps at every prime and stays flat in between.

The aim of the current chapter is to obtain lower and upper bounds for $\pi(x)$. In order to do this we recall some key results regarding $^{2n}C_n$ obtained in earlier chapters that shall be of use here, where p is always used to denote a prime:

$$\frac{2^{2n-1}}{n} < \binom{2n}{n} < 2^{2n} \text{ for } n \geq 2. \qquad \text{(Result 2.5)}$$

$$\prod_{n<p\leq 2n} p \ \middle| \ \binom{2n}{n}. \qquad \text{(2.1 from Result 2.6(a))}$$

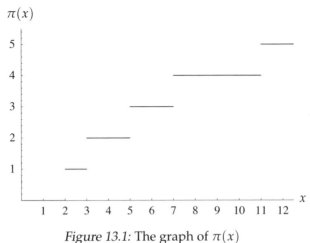

Figure 13.1: The graph of $\pi(x)$

If $f(p)$ is the unique non-negative integer satisfying $p^{f(p)} \le 2n < p^{f(p)+1}$ then

$$\binom{2n}{n} \left| \prod_{p \le 2n} p^{f(p)} \right. \qquad \text{(Result 4.2)}$$

The above will now be used to help prove an amazing and rather deep result on the distribution of the primes.

Result 13.1 *Let $n \ge 2$. Then*

$$\frac{n}{8 \ln n} < \pi(n) < \frac{6n}{\ln n}.$$

PROOF It will first be shown that

$$n^{\pi(2n)-\pi(n)} < \prod_{n<p\le 2n} p. \qquad (13.1)$$

Let us give careful consideration to the inequality (13.1) since there is rather a lot to take in here. The term on the left is n to the power of the number of primes between n and $2n$ (noting that $2n$ is not prime for $n \ge 2$) while the term on the right is the product of all the primes between n and $2n$. The inequality is always true since the expressions on each side may be regarded as the product of $\pi(2n) - \pi(n)$ numbers, where each of the numbers in the product on the right is greater than each of the numbers in the product on the left (all of which are n). Let us, for example, take $n = 10$. In this case the primes between n and $2n$ are 11, 13, 17 and 19 so that $\pi(2n) - \pi(n) = 4$. Thus

$$n^{\pi(2n)-\pi(n)} = 10^4 = 10 \times 10 \times 10 \times 10$$

while

$$\prod_{n<p\leq 2n} p = 11 \times 13 \times 17 \times 19.$$

If (13.1) is used in conjunction with Result 2.5 and (2.1) we obtain

$$n^{\pi(2n)-\pi(n)} < \prod_{n<p\leq 2n} p \leq \binom{2n}{n} < 2^{2n}. \tag{13.2}$$

Next, it is true that

$$\prod_{p\leq 2n} p^{f(p)} < (2n)^{\pi(2n)}. \tag{13.3}$$

This is because if $p \leq 2n$ then, from the definition of $f(p)$, $2n \geq p^{f(p)}$ so each of the $\pi(2n)$ numbers of the form $p^{f(p)}$ in the product on the left will be no greater than each of the $\pi(2n)$ numbers in the product on the right (all of which are $2n$). Combining (13.3), Result 2.5 and Result 4.2 leads to the following chain of inequalities

$$(2n)^{\pi(2n)} \geq \prod_{p\leq 2n} p^{f(p)} \geq \binom{2n}{n} > \frac{2^{2n-1}}{n} \geq 2^n. \tag{13.4}$$

Substituting $n = 2^k$ in (13.4) gives

$$\left(2 \times 2^k\right)^{\pi(2\times 2^k)} > 2^{2^k},$$

which simplifies to

$$\left(2^{k+1}\right)^{\pi(2^{k+1})} > 2^{2^k}. \tag{13.5}$$

On considering the exponents of 2 on both sides of inequality (13.5) we obtain the result

$$(k+1)\pi\left(2^{k+1}\right) > 2^k. \tag{13.6}$$

Challenge 13.1   Put $n = 2^k$ in (13.2) and show that

$$k\left[\pi\left(2^{k+1}\right) - \pi\left(2^k\right)\right] < 2^{k+1}.$$

Challenge 13.2   Show that $\pi(2^{k+1}) \leq 2^k$.

Using the result of Challenge 13.2 with that of Challenge 13.1 gives

$$k\left[\pi(2^{k+1}) - \pi(2^k)\right] + \pi(2^{k+1}) < 2^{k+1} + 2^k$$

so that

$$(k+1)\pi(2^{k+1}) - k\pi(2^k) < 2^k(2+1) = 2^k \times 3. \tag{13.7}$$

Summing both sides of (13.7) from $k = 0$ to $k = m$ leads to the following result

$$\sum_{k=0}^{m}\left[(k+1)\pi(2^{k+1}) - k\pi(2^k)\right] < 3\sum_{k=0}^{m} 2^k < 3 \times 2^{m+1}, \tag{13.8}$$

where the right-hand inequality arises from the fact that $\sum_{k=0}^{m} 2^k = 2^{m+1} - 1$. However,

$$\sum_{k=0}^{m}\left[(k+1)\pi(2^{k+1}) - k\pi(2^k)\right] =$$

$$1 \times \pi(2) - 0 \times \pi(1)$$
$$+2 \times \pi(4) - 1 \times \pi(2)$$
$$+3 \times \pi(8) - 2 \times \pi(4)$$
$$\vdots$$
$$+(m+1) \times \pi(2^{m+1}) - m \times \pi(2^m)$$
$$= (m+1) \times \pi(2^{m+1})$$

(the nice collapsing procedure seen above is sometimes called 'telescoping'), from which it follows, in combination with (13.8), that

$$(m+1)\pi(2^{m+1}) < 3 \times 2^{m+1}.$$

This, along with (13.6), shows that

$$\frac{2^{m+1}}{2(m+1)} < \pi(2^{m+1}) < \frac{3 \times 2^{m+1}}{m+1}. \tag{13.9}$$

Finally, given any $n \geq 2$, we choose m such that $2^{m+1} \leq n < 2^{m+2}$. Then, on using the right-hand inequality of (13.9), it follows that

$$\pi(n) \leq \pi(2^{m+2}) < \frac{3 \times 2^{m+2}}{m+2} < \frac{6 \times 2^{m+1}}{(m+2)\ln 2},$$

where the fact that $\ln 2 < 1$ has been used in the last inequality. However, since $2^{m+1} \leq n < 2^{m+2}$, we obtain

$$\frac{6 \times 2^{m+1}}{(m+2)\ln 2} = \frac{6 \times 2^{m+1}}{\ln(2^{m+2})} \leq \frac{6n}{\ln(2^{m+2})} < \frac{6n}{\ln n}$$

and thus

$$\pi(n) < \frac{6n}{\ln n}.$$

Similarly, by considering the left-hand inequality of (13.9), the following result emerges

$$\pi(n) \geq \pi(2^{m+1}) > \frac{2^{m+1}}{2(m+1)} = \frac{2^{m+2}}{4(m+1)}$$
$$> \frac{n}{8(m+1)\ln 2} = \frac{n}{8\ln(2^{m+1})}$$
$$\geq \frac{n}{8\ln n},$$

thereby completing the proof. ❑

It really does seem remarkable that so much information about the distribution of the primes can be obtained with such ease (relatively speaking). You could be forgiven for thinking initially that Result 13.1 is actually a rather useless result since the upper bound it gives for $\pi(n)$ is greater than the lower bound by a factor of 48. However, the key thing is that this ratio between the lower bound and the upper bound is independent of n. This means that Result 13.1 is telling us that $\pi(n)$ behaves approximately like $\frac{n}{\ln n}$.

One of the all-time great theorems of mathematics is the Prime Number Theorem (PNT), which says that

$$\frac{\pi(n)\ln n}{n} \to 1 \text{ as } n \to \infty,$$

or, in other words, that $\pi(n) \sim \frac{n}{\ln n}$. This theorem was proved by Jacques Hadamard and Charles de la Vallée Poussin at the end of the 19th century.

Amazingly enough their proofs were obtained independently and virtually simultaneously (both in 1896). You will now see that Result 13.1 can actually be thought of as a 'poor relation' to the PNT since it tells us that the order of magnitude of $\pi(n)$ is $\frac{n}{\ln n}$ but is not sufficient to tell us that $\frac{\pi(n)\ln n}{n} \to 1$ as $n \to \infty$. The PNT is certainly a difficult theorem, and to understand it fully requires a considerable step up from the mathematics that we are doing here.

The first proofs of the PNT incorporated results from complex analysis and it was not until 1949 that a so-called 'elementary' proof was obtained. Unfortunately this proved to be a somewhat controversial event in the history of mathematics. Two mathematicians, the Norwegian Atle Selberg and the Hungarian Paul Erdös, contributed to the elementary proof of the PNT. However, Selberg went ahead and published it without Erdös, thereby receiving the bulk of the credit. In fact, Selberg was then even awarded the Fields Medal shortly afterwards (there is no Nobel Prize in Mathematics but the Fields Medal is regarded as equivalent to it).

Research Activity 13.1   Despite the technical difficulties of the proof itself, you will find it well worth your while looking into the PNT and its history.

Exercise 13

1. Evaluate exactly:

    (a) $\pi(23)$ (b) $\pi(\sqrt{48})$ (c) $\pi(100)$

2. What information does Chebyshev's inequality (Result 13.1) give us about $\pi(100)$? In other words, what is the largest integer a and the smallest integer b it yields such that $a \le \pi(100) \le b$? What about $\pi(1\,000\,000)$?

3. (a) Use the fact that 2 is the only even prime to show that $\pi(n) \le \frac{n}{2}$ for all positive integers n.

(b) Find the smallest positive integer n such that Chebyshev's inequality gives an improvement on the upper bound for $\pi(n)$ given in part (a).

4. Use the Prime Number Theorem to obtain a rough estimate of the number of primes between $5\,000\,000$ and $6\,000\,000$.

5. Show, by finding a counterexample, that the following statement is false:

   "$\pi(m + n) < \pi(m) + \pi(n)$ for all integers m and n with $5 \leq m \leq n$."

6. Assuming the Prime Number Theorem

$$\frac{\pi(n)\ln n}{n} \to 1 \text{ as } n \to \infty,$$

try to figure out a way of showing that

$$\frac{p_n}{n \ln n} \to 1 \text{ as } n \to \infty,$$

where p_n is the nth prime number.

Chapter 14

Bertrand's postulate

In order to introduce this next idea, let us list, in order, all the primes below 100:

$$2, 3, 5, 7, 11, 13, 17, 19, 23, 29, 31, 37, 41,$$
$$43, 47, 53, 59, 61, 67, 71, 73, 79, 83, 89, 97.$$

Now choose any integer n you like from 1 to 50 inclusive. Is there a prime on the above list larger than n yet no larger than $2n$? Your answer should be in the affirmative. That this is generally true was first conjectured by the French mathematician Joseph Bertrand (1822-1900) in 1845. Although he carried out a numerical verification for all integers up to about three million, he was not able to prove his postulate.

Before getting involved in the mathematics, there is something very interesting that we ought to point out about the title 'Bertrand's postulate'. It should not actually be called a postulate any more since it has been proved and is thus now a theorem. In fact, it is sometimes referred to as Chebyshev's theorem, after Pafnuty Chebyshev (1821-1894), the Russian mathematician whom we met in the previous chapter, who did actually prove the conjecture in 1850. This is one of those theorems that has been proved many times since Chebyshev first proved it. Simpler versions were given by such mathematical greats as Srinivasa Ramanujan (1887-1920) from India and Paul Erdös (1913-1996) from Hungary. Indeed, the proof we present here is essentially the one that Erdös came up with at the age of just 19.

Research Activity 14.1   Some characters in the history of mathematics are particularly fascinating, and the two mentioned at the end of the last paragraph are really worth reading about. Ramanujan was certainly a genius. When the great English mathematician Godfrey Hardy (1877-1947) was asked to rate mathematicians out of 100 he rated himself at 25, the outstanding German mathematician David Hilbert (1862-1943) at 80 and Ramanujan at 100. Despite the fact that Hardy, one of the foremost mathematicians in England at the time, was probably being somewhat modest in rating himself at 25, it is obvious that he regarded Ramanujan's mathematical gifts with awe. Recent biographies of Erdös and Ramanujan that I can recommend are [8] and [9], respectively. As well as the biographies, there is now a play (see the website [4]).

In this chapter it is proved that if n is any positive integer then there exists a prime p satisfying $n < p \leq 2n$. In order to prove this we shall need, as well as some of our previous results, three further results. The first of these concerns the product of all the primes no larger than n while the next two provide some information about the prime factorisation of $^{2n}C_n$.

Result 14.1
$$\prod_{p \leq n} p < 4^{n-1} \text{ for } n \geq 2.$$

PROOF To show that this is true we proceed by induction. The truth of the above proposition for $n = 2$ and $n = 3$ is easily checked. It is also clear that if the proposition is true when n is an odd integer greater than 1 (say $n = 2m - 1$, where $m \geq 2$) then

$$\prod_{p \leq 2m} p = \prod_{p \leq 2m-1} p < 4^{2m-2} < 4^{2m-1},$$

since $2m$ will not be a prime. For example, if $m = 7$ then

$$\prod_{p \leq 2m} p = \prod_{p \leq 14} p = 2 \times 3 \times 5 \times 7 \times 11 \times 13 = \prod_{p \leq 13} p = \prod_{p \leq 2m-1} p$$

so if it is true that

$$\prod_{p \leq 13} p < 4^{12}$$

then it is also true that

$$\prod_{p \leq 14} p < 4^{12} < 4^{13}.$$

In other words, the truth of the proposition for odd n greater than 1 implies its truth for $n + 1$. So all we need to do is to prove that the proposition is true when n is odd.

With this in mind, let $n = 2m + 1$ where $m \geq 2$ and let us assume that

$$\prod_{p \leq n} p < 4^{n-1}$$

for all integers n such that $2 \leq n \leq 2m$. Note that every prime from $m + 2$ to $2m + 1$ inclusive divides $^{2m+1}C_m$. To see this it is easiest to write out $^{2m+1}C_m$ as

$$\binom{2m+1}{m} = \frac{(2m+1)!}{m!(m+1)!} = \frac{(2m+1) \times 2m \times \cdots \times (m+2)}{m \times (m-1) \times \cdots \times 1},$$

from which it is clear that if any of the factors from $m + 2$ to $2m + 1$ appearing in the numerator are primes then it will be impossible to cancel them out with terms in the denominator. From this it follows that

$$\prod_{m+2 \leq p \leq 2m+1} p \quad \middle| \quad \binom{2m+1}{m}$$

and hence that

$$\prod_{m+2 \leq p \leq 2m+1} p \leq \binom{2m+1}{m}$$

Using this result in conjunction with the inductive hypothesis gives

$$\prod_{p \leq 2m+1} p = \prod_{m+2 \leq p \leq 2m+1} p \quad \times \prod_{p \leq m+1} p$$

$$\leq \binom{2m+1}{m} \prod_{p \leq m+1} p$$

$$< \binom{2m+1}{m} 4^m.$$

From the above it can be seen that the proof would be complete if it could be shown that $^{2m+1}C_m \geq 4^m$. To this end, we have

$$4^{m+1} = 2 \times 2^{2m+1}$$

$$= 2(1+1)^{2m+1}$$

$$= 2\left[\binom{2m+1}{0} + \cdots + \binom{2m+1}{m} + \binom{2m+1}{m+1}\right.$$

$$\left. + \cdots + \binom{2m+1}{2m+1}\right],$$

so that

$$\binom{2m+1}{m} + \binom{2m+1}{m+1} < \frac{4^{m+1}}{2},$$

and hence, on noting that $^{2m+1}C_m = {}^{2m+1}C_{m+1}$ by the symmetry property (1.1), that

$$\binom{2m+1}{m} < \frac{4^{m+1}}{4} = 4^m,$$

as required. Thus, by the principle of mathematical induction, we have shown that

$$\prod_{p \leq n} p < 4^{n-1}$$

for all $n \geq 2$. $\qquad\qquad\qquad\qquad\qquad\qquad\qquad\qquad\qquad\qquad\qquad\qquad\qquad$ ❏

Result 14.2 *Let $e(p)$ be the exponent of p in the prime factorisation of $^{2n}C_n$ (that is, $p^{e(p)}$ divides $^{2n}C_n$ but $p^{e(p)+1}$ does not). Then $p^{e(p)} \leq 2n$.*

PROOF To show this we use a result obtained earlier (Result 4.2):

If $f(p)$ satisfies $p^{f(p)} \leq 2n < p^{f(p)+1}$ then the power of p in the prime factorisation of $^{2n}C_n$ cannot exceed $f(p)$.

From this it follows that $p^{e(p)} \leq p^{f(p)} \leq 2n$, as required. $\qquad\qquad\qquad$ ❏

Result 14.3 *Any prime factor p of $^{2n}C_n$ for which $e(p) > 1$ cannot exceed $\lfloor\sqrt{2n}\rfloor$. Consequently there are less than $\lfloor\sqrt{2n}\rfloor$ primes in the prime factorisation of $^{2n}C_n$ having an exponent greater than 1.*

PROOF In order to prove this, suppose that p is a prime factor of $^{2n}C_n$ for which $e(p) \geq 2$. From Result 14.2 we know that $p^{e(p)} \leq 2n$, so that

$$p \leq \sqrt{2n} \text{ when } e(p) > 1.$$

From this it can be seen, remembering that 1 is not a prime, that there are less than $\lfloor \sqrt{2n} \rfloor$ primes in the prime factorisation of $^{2n}C_n$ with an exponent greater than 1. ❑

We are now going to prove Bertrand's postulate. This is a little more involved and intricate than anything else done up to this point, but please persevere. It will be worth the effort, and you will improve as a mathematician as a result of your hard work. The method of proof used here is generally termed 'proof by contradiction'. We assume that the postulate is false and show that this leads to mathematical nonsense, from which we are forced to conclude that our initial assumption must be false and consequently that the postulate is true.

It is easily checked that the postulate is true for $n = 1, 2$ and 3. Now suppose that it is false for some $n > 3$. In other words, suppose that there exists some n such that there is no prime p satisfying the condition $n < p \leq 2n$. Let us consider what this means in the light of one of our previous results (Result 2.6(b)):

If $\frac{2n}{3} < p \leq n$ then p does not appear in the prime factorisation of $^{2n}C_n$ when $n \geq 3$.

Remembering, from the work in Chapter 4, that $^{2n}C_n$ possesses no prime factors greater than $2n$, it can be seen that our assumption in conjunction with the above result implies that any prime factor p of $^{2n}C_n$ satisfies the condition $p \leq \frac{2n}{3}$.

We next obtain, under the assumption that Bertrand's postulate is not true for some n, an upper bound for the size of $^{2n}C_n$ by considering its prime factorisation:

Result 14.4 *Suppose that Bertrand's postulate is false for some n. Then*

$$\binom{2n}{n} < (2n)^{\lfloor \sqrt{2n} \rfloor} \prod_{p \leq \frac{2n}{3}} p.$$

PROOF We already know, under the above assumption, that any prime factor p of $^{2n}C_n$ satisfies the condition $p \leq \frac{2n}{3}$. Thus the contribution from all the primes with exponent 1 in the prime factorisation of to that prime factorisation can be no more than

$$\prod_{p \leq \frac{2n}{3}} p.$$

Also, by Result 14.3, it follows that the contribution from the primes with exponent greater than 1 in the prime factorisation of $^{2n}C_n$ to that prime factorisation is equal to

$$\prod_{p \leq \sqrt{2n}} p^{e(p)} \, .$$

However,

$$\prod_{p \leq \sqrt{2n}} p^{e(p)} \leq \prod_{p \leq \sqrt{2n}} 2n \leq \prod_{k=2}^{\lfloor \sqrt{2n} \rfloor} 2n < \prod_{k=1}^{\lfloor \sqrt{2n} \rfloor} 2n = (2n)^{\lfloor \sqrt{2n} \rfloor},$$

where Result 14.2 has been used in the first step. Thus, by considering the contributions from all of the primes in the prime factorisation of $^{2n}C_n$, the following inequality emerges

$$\binom{2n}{n} < (2n)^{\lfloor \sqrt{2n} \rfloor} \prod_{p \leq \frac{2n}{3}} p \, .$$

❑

Using Result 2.5 and Result 14.4 with Result 14.1 gives

$$\frac{4^n}{2n} < \binom{2n}{n} < (2n)^{\lfloor \sqrt{2n} \rfloor} \prod_{p \leq \frac{2n}{3}} p < (2n)^{\sqrt{2n}} 4^{\lfloor \frac{2n}{3} \rfloor - 1},$$

from which we obtain

$$4^{n - \lfloor \frac{2n}{3} \rfloor + 1} < (2n)^{1 + \sqrt{2n}}. \tag{14.1}$$

The next task is to show that there exists some positive integer N such that the inequality (14.1) does not actually hold for any $n \geq N$. Since

$$n - \left\lfloor \frac{2n}{3} \right\rfloor + 1 \geq \frac{n+3}{3},$$

it follows, on taking logarithms of both sides of (14.1), that

$$\tfrac{1}{3}(n+3) \ln 4 < \left(1 + \sqrt{2n}\right) \ln(2n).$$

With a little trial and error on a calculator, it is found that the smallest value of n for which this inequality is not true is 460. In fact, by considering the functions on either side of the inequality, it is clear that this does not hold for $n \geq 460$.

Now, in order to complete the proof, we just need to check that Bertrand's postulate does in fact hold for $1 \le n \le 459$. It is possible to do this without performing an individual check for each of these 459 values of n, as follows.

Consider the sequence of primes given by

$$2, 3, 5, 7, 13, 23, 43, 83, 163, 317, 631$$

for which each term is generated by taking the largest prime not exceeding double the previous one, denoting them by $p_1 = 2$, $p_2 = 3$, ..., $p_{11} = 631$. If m is any integer such that $2 \le m \le 459$ then we can find consecutive terms in the above sequence, p_k and p_{k+1} say, such that $p_k \le m < p_{k+1}$. Since $p_{k+1} < 2p_k$ it must be the case that

$$p_k \le m < p_{k+1} < 2p_k \le 2m,$$

from which it can be seen that $m < p_{k+1} < 2m$. The remaining case to be considered is $m = 1$, and since Bertrand's postulate is true in this case we have completed the proof.

Chapter 15

An interesting divisibility property of $^{2p}C_p - 2$

A numerical investigation reveals the following results:

$$\binom{10}{5} = 252 \qquad = 2 \times 5^3 + 2,$$

$$\binom{14}{7} = 3\,432 \qquad = 100 \times 7^3 + 2,$$

$$\binom{22}{11} = 705\,432 \qquad = 530 \times 11^3 + 2,$$

$$\binom{26}{13} = 10\,400\,600 = 4\,734 \times 13^3 + 2.$$

Although the above does not give us an awful lot to go on, it might be conjectured from this that p^3 always divides $^{2p}C_p - 2$ for $p \geq 5$. Indeed, calculations reveal that this pattern does continue for the next few primes beyond 13. It turns out that this conjecture is in fact true (a result that is, in my opinion at least, far from obvious), and the aim of this chapter is show that this is the case. You will encounter two proofs here, the first of which is covered in considerable detail. The second takes the form of an extended task/challenge, giving you the opportunity to construct the proof yourself with the help of an outline and some hints.

The first proof is based on a method given in [3]. We let p be any prime such that $p \geq 5$ and define the polynomial $f(x)$ of degree $p - 1$ as follows:

$$f(x) = (x+1)(x+2)(x+3)\ldots(x+p-1). \qquad (15.1)$$

If $f(x)$ is expanded then it can be written as

$$f(x) = x^{p-1} + a_{p-2}x^{p-2} + \cdots + a_1 x + a_0,$$

where the coefficients $a_0, a_1, a_2, \ldots, a_{p-2}$ are necessarily all positive integers. We now prove a divisibility property of the coefficients $a_1, a_2, \ldots,$ a_{p-2}, utilising the following simple algebraic property of $f(x)$:

$$\begin{aligned}
(x+p)f(x) &= (x+1)(x+2)(x+3)\ldots(x+p-1)(x+p) \\
&= (x+1)\{([x+1]+1)([x+1]+2) \\
&\qquad \ldots ([x+1]+p-2)([x+1]+p-1)\} \\
&= (x+1)f(x+1). \qquad (15.2)
\end{aligned}$$

Result 15.1 *The coefficients $a_1, a_2, \ldots, a_{p-2}$ are each divisible by p.*

PROOF Let k be any integer such that $2 \leq k \leq p - 1$. On writing

$$\begin{aligned}
(x+p)f(x) = \; &x\big(x^{p-1} + a_{p-2}x^{p-2} + \cdots + a_1 x + a_0\big) \\
&+ p\big(x^{p-1} + a_{p-2}x^{p-2} + \cdots + a_1 x + a_0\big),
\end{aligned}$$

it can be seen that the coefficient of x^{p-k} in $(x+p)f(x)$ is $a_{p-k-1} + p a_{p-k}$. Also, since

$$\begin{aligned}
(x+1)f(x+1) &= (x+1)\big[(x+1)^{p-1} + a_{p-2}(x+1)^{p-2} \\
&\qquad\qquad + \cdots + a_1(x+1) + a_0\big] \\
&= (x+1)^p + a_{p-2}(x+1)^{p-1} \\
&\qquad\qquad + \cdots + a_1(x+1)^2 + a_0(x+1),
\end{aligned}$$

it follows, on using the binomial theorem, that the coefficient of x^{p-k} in $(x+1)f(x+1)$ is given by

$$\binom{p}{p-k} + a_{p-2}\binom{p-1}{p-k} + a_{p-3}\binom{p-2}{p-k} + \cdots + a_{p-k-1}\binom{p-k}{p-k}.$$

Let us now equate the coefficients of $x^{p-2}, x^{p-3}, x^{p-4}, \ldots, x$ on both sides of (15.2) in turn. First

$$a_{p-3} + p a_{p-2} - \binom{p}{p-2} \mid a_{p-2}\binom{p-1}{p-2} + a_p \,_3\binom{p-2}{p-2}.$$

which simplifies to

$$pa_{p-2} = \binom{p}{p-2} + (p-1)a_{p-2}$$

and then further to

$$a_{p-2} = \binom{p}{p-2} = \frac{p(p-1)}{2}.$$

This shows, as a consequence of the fact that $p \geq 5$, that a_{p-2} is divisible by p.

Next we equate the coefficient of x^{p-k} on both sides of (15.2), where $3 \leq k \leq p-1$, to obtain

$$a_{p-k-1} + pa_{p-k} = \binom{p}{p-k} + a_{p-2}\binom{p-1}{p-k} + a_{p-3}\binom{p-2}{p-k}$$
$$+ \cdots + a_{p-k-1}\binom{p-k}{p-k}.$$

After simplifying this gives

$$pa_{p-k} = \binom{p}{p-k} + a_{p-2}\binom{p-1}{p-k} + a_{p-3}\binom{p-2}{p-k}$$
$$+ \cdots + a_{p-k}\binom{p-k+1}{p-k},$$

and then

$$(k-1)a_{p-k} = \binom{p}{p-k} + a_{p-2}\binom{p-1}{p-k} + a_{p-3}\binom{p-2}{p-k}$$
$$+ \cdots + a_{p-k+1}\binom{p-k+2}{p-k}, \quad (15.3)$$

With $k = 3$ there will be just two terms on the right-hand side of (15.3). The first term on the right is divisible by p, as is the second term (remembering that we have already shown that p divides a_{p-2}). Then, since p does not divide $k - 1 = 2$, (15.3) implies that a_{p-3} is divisible by p. A similar argument applies when $k = 4$, in which case there will three terms on the right-hand side of (15.3), each of which is divisible by p. We can keep going right up to $k = p - 1$ in order to obtain the result that each of $a_1, a_2, \ldots, a_{p-2}$ is divisible by p. ❑

We now have all we need to prove the divisibility result:

Result 15.2 p^3 *divides* $\binom{2p}{p}$ - 2 *for all* $p \geq 5$.

PROOF First

$$f(p) = (p+1)(p+2)(p+3)\ldots(2p-1)$$

and

$$
\begin{aligned}
f(-2p) &= (-2p+1)(-2p+2)(-2p+3)\ldots(-2p+p-1)\\
&= \left(-[2p-1]\right)\left(-[2p-2]\right)\left(-[2p-3]\right)\ldots\left(-[p+1]\right)\\
&= (-1)^{p-1}(2p-1)(2p-2)(2p-3)\ldots(p+1)\\
&= (2p-1)(2p-2)(2p-3)\ldots(p+1)
\end{aligned}
$$

on noting that $(-1)^{p-1} = 1$ since $p-1$ is even. Thus

$$f(p) - f(-2p) = 0$$

so that

$$
p^{p-1} + a_{p-2}p^{p-2} + \cdots + a_1 p + a_0 \\
\qquad - (-2p)^{p-1} - a_{p-2}(-2p)^{p-2} - \cdots - a_1(-2p) - a_0 = 0
$$

which rearranges to

$$
3pa_1 = p^{p-1} + a_{p-2}p^{p-2} + \cdots + a_2 p^2 \\
\qquad - (-2p)^{p-1} - a_{p-2}(-2p)^{p-2} - \cdots - a_2(-2p)^2.
$$

From Result 15.1 we know that each of the terms on the right-hand side is divisible by, so that $3pa_1$ is divisible by p^3. Then, since $p \geq 5$, it can be seen that a_1 is divisible by p^2.

The above fact tells us that each of the terms in

$$f(p) = p^{p-1} + a_{p-2}p^{p-2} + \cdots + a_1 p + a_0$$

is divisible by p^3 except for the term

$$a_0 = f(0) = (0+1)(0+2)(0+3)\ldots(0+p-1) = (p-1)!$$

Therefore p^3 divides

$$\begin{aligned} f(p) - a_0 &= (p+1)(p+2)(p+3)\ldots(2p-1) - (p-1)! \\ &= \frac{(2p-1)!}{p!} - (p-1)! \\ &= \frac{p!}{2p}\left[\frac{2p(2p-1)!}{(p!)^2} - \frac{2p(p-1)!}{p!}\right] \\ &= \frac{(p-1)!}{2}\left[\binom{2p}{p} - 2\right]. \end{aligned}$$

Then, since p is not a factor of $\frac{1}{2}(p-1)!$, it follows that

$$p^3 \,\Bigg|\, \binom{2p}{p} - 2$$

as required.   ❑

This is closely related to another divisibility result which is called *Wolstenholme's theorem*. You can read about this on the website [16].

Using some of the results already obtained in this chapter, it is possible to prove two well-known theorems from the field of Number Theory, namely *Wilson's theorem* and *Fermat's little theorem*. In Exercise 15 we ask you to prove both of them. In order to understand these theorems and the extended research task that concludes this chapter you need to know a little about *modular arithmetic* and the *theory of congruences*.

Research Activity 15.1   In many problems of Number Theory we are interested only in the remainder when one number is divided by another. If two positive integers m and n leave the same remainder when divided by the positive integer k then they may, in some sense, be regarded as equivalent with respect to k. In this case m and n are said to be 'congruent modulo k', and this is written as $m \equiv n \pmod{k}$. To take an example, 32 and 17 both leave remainder 2 when divided by 5 so $32 \equiv 17 \equiv 2 \pmod{5}$. Arithmetic carried out in these circumstances is called *modular arithmetic*.

This idea gives rise to an area of Number Theory called the *theory of congruences*. Some results associated with congruences will be needed for what follows. As mentioned in the preface, we would recommend the book [1] as giving a good introduction to this area (and to elementary number theory in general). If you want to take things a bit further then [7] is also well worth looking at.

To give a specific example of a result that we shall be using, it may be noted that if $km \equiv kn \pmod{12}$ then it is not necessarily the case that $m \equiv n \pmod{12}$, as can be seen on considering the congruence $8 \times 6 \equiv 8 \times 3 \pmod{12}$. However, if k and 12 have no common prime factors (we write this as $\gcd(k, 12) = 1$) then $km \equiv kn \pmod{12}$ does imply that $m \equiv n \pmod{12}$. Thus $7m \equiv 7n \pmod{12}$, for example, implies that $m \equiv n \pmod{12}$.

We have now almost reached the end of our journey along the Backbone of Pascal's Triangle. The aim of this book has been to explore many of the rich mathematical ideas associated with a particular sequence of numbers, the central binomial coefficients. To this point you will have faced a multitude of problems, from relatively simple ones to those requiring a considerable amount of time and effort. I would like to leave you with an activity that goes one step further.

The following extended piece of work might be regarded as a more long-term mathematics project. Many of the proofs in this book are as the result of other people's hard work, but you will find that it is always particularly satisfying to come up with your own proof of a 'well-known' result, even though there might be more elegant proofs around. The alternative proof of Result 15.2 outlined below is my own. It has been split into several steps. Your final task is to fill in all the details for each step and hence construct a water-tight proof from this outline. The work takes us into some new mathematical territories so you will need to do a little research along the way.

Extended Challenge/Research Activity

(1) Show first that p^2 divides $^{2p}C_p - 2$ for all $p \geq 5$. In order to do this you can use Result 2.2 to obtain the result

$$\binom{2p}{p} - 2 = \sum_{k=0}^{p} \binom{p}{k}^2 - 2 = \sum_{k=1}^{p-1} \binom{p}{k}^2$$

and then show that p^2 divides each of the terms in the sum on the right.

It is now clear that if it could be proved that p divides the sum

$$\sum_{k=1}^{p-1} \frac{1}{p^2} \binom{p}{k}^2$$

then it would follow that p^3 always divides $^{2p}C_p - 2$ for $p \geq 5$. To prove that p does actually divide this sum is rather tricky and requires several more steps.

(2) In order to tackle the current proof of Result 15.2 you need to know a little about *quadratic residues*. This has to do with the remainders of square numbers when they are divided by primes. To be more precise, if p is a prime and n is a number such that $\gcd(n, p) = 1$ then n is said to be a 'quadratic residue modulo p' if there exists an integer m such that $m^2 \equiv n \pmod{p}$. For example, we say that 2 is a quadratic residue modulo 7 since $3^2 \equiv 2 \pmod 7$. On the other hand, as you can easily check, 3 is not a quadratic residue modulo 7. Once more, [1] gives a good introduction to this aspect of Number Theory.

(3) Now let us consider the terms in the sum

$$\sum_{k=1}^{p-1} \frac{1}{p^2} \binom{p}{k}^2.$$

Suppose that

$$\frac{1}{p^2} \binom{p}{n}^2 \equiv \frac{1}{p^2} \binom{p}{m}^2 \pmod{p} \quad \text{with } 1 \leq m, n \leq p - 1,$$

where, without loss of generality, $n \geq m$. Show that

$$\text{either} \quad \frac{1}{p} \binom{p}{n} \equiv \frac{1}{p} \binom{p}{m} \pmod{p} \tag{15.4}$$

$$\text{or} \quad \frac{1}{p} \binom{p}{n} \equiv -\frac{1}{p} \binom{p}{m} \pmod{p} \tag{15.5}$$

(4) Next show that (15.4) and (15.5) imply

$$(-1)^{n-m} m \equiv n \pmod{p} \tag{15.6}$$

$$\text{and} \quad (-1)^{n-m+1} m \equiv n \pmod{p}, \tag{15.7}$$

respectively.

(5) You now need to know what is meant by 'a full set of quadratic residues modulo p'. This is best explained by way of an example. Let us set $p = 13$ and consider the possible values that squares of integers can take modulo 13. For example,

$$4^2 = 16 \equiv 3 \pmod{13} \quad \text{and} \quad 21^2 = 441 \equiv 12 \pmod{13}.$$

As mentioned in (2) above, 3 and 12 are called *quadratic residues modulo 13*. You should check for yourself that there are in fact six quadratic residues modulo 13, namely 1, 3, 4, 9, 10 and 12. The set $\{1, 3, 4, 9, 10, 12\}$ is therefore called a full set of quadratic residues modulo 13. It turns out that in general there are exactly $\frac{p-1}{2}$ distinct quadratic residues modulo p. See [1, Chapter 9] for further details.

(6) Now use (15.6) (noting that neither (15.7) nor, as a consequence, (15.5) are possible) to prove that if

$$\frac{1}{p^2}\binom{p}{n}^2 \equiv \frac{1}{p^2}\binom{p}{m}^2 \pmod{p}, \quad \text{with } 1 \leq m, n \leq p - 1$$

then either $m = n$ or $m = p - n$, and hence

$$\left\{ \frac{1}{p^2}\binom{p}{k}^2 \pmod{p} : 1 \leq k \leq \tfrac{p-1}{2} \right\}$$

$$\text{and} \quad \left\{ \frac{1}{p^2}\binom{p}{k}^2 \pmod{p} : \tfrac{p+1}{2} \leq k \leq p - 1 \right\}$$

both give a full set of quadratic residues modulo p.

(7) It is well-known (again, see [1]) that a full set of quadratic residues modulo p is given by $\left\{ k^2 \pmod{p} : 1 \leq k \leq \tfrac{p-1}{2} \right\}$. Use this fact to obtain the result

$$\sum_{k=1}^{p-1} \frac{1}{p^2}\binom{p}{k}^2 \equiv \frac{1}{12}p(p-1)(p+1) \pmod{p}.$$

(8) To complete the proof show that $\frac{1}{12}p(p-1)(p+1)$ is an integer multiple of p when p is a prime with $p \geq 5$.

Exercise 15

(Note: This exercise is a little more demanding than previous ones.)

1. Show that Result 15.2 generalises to

$$p^3 \text{ divides } \binom{np}{p} - n \text{ for all } p \geq 5 \text{ and } n \geq 1.$$

2. Use the results obtained in this chapter to prove Wilson's theorem, which tells us that if p is any prime then $(p - 1)! \equiv -1 \pmod{p}$.

3. (a) Now prove Fermat's little theorem which says that if p is a prime and n is a positive integer that does not have p as a factor then $n^{p-1} \equiv 1 \pmod{p}$.

   (b) Hence show that if p is an odd prime then it is a factor of

$$1^p + 2^p + 3^p + \cdots + (p-1)^p.$$

4. Find, using the following method, the remainder when 6^{546} is divided by 17:

   Step 1: Express 6^{546} in the form 6^{16k+m} for the smallest possible non-negative integer m.

   Step 2: Use Fermat's little theorem to show that

$$6^{16k+m} \equiv 6^m \pmod{17}.$$

   Step 3: Find an integer j with $0 \leq j \leq 16$ such that

$$6^m \equiv j \pmod{17}.$$

5. Similarly, calculate the remainder when 2^{1229} is divided by 103.

6. Show that 7 divides $12^{51} + 1$.

7. (a) Employ Wilson's theorem to help you find the remainder when 21! is divided by 23.

   (b) Generalise your result from part (a).

8. Let k be an integer with $k \geq 2$. Show that if it satisfies

$$(k-1)! \equiv -1 \pmod{k}$$

then k is a prime number (this is the converse to Wilson's theorem).

Appendices

Appendix A

Proof by induction

The following example gives a good illustration of the method of proof by induction, and the logic behind it. Consider the expression $f(n) = 5^n - 1$. Since

$$f(1) = 5^1 - 1 = 4,$$
$$f(2) = 5^2 - 1 = 24 = 6 \times 4,$$
$$\text{and} \quad f(3) = 5^3 - 1 = 124 = 31 \times 4,$$

it might be conjectured that $f(n) = 5^n - 1$ is divisible by 4 for all positive integers n.

Let us suppose that it is indeed true that $f(n) = 5^n - 1$ is divisible by 4 when $n = k$ for some positive integer k (this supposition is called the *inductive hypothesis*). We look to see whether this has any implications with regard to $f(k+1)$. To this end, $f(k+1)$ can be rearranged as follows:

$$f(k+1) = 5^{k+1} - 1$$
$$= 5 \times 5^k - 1$$
$$= 5(5^k - 1) + 5 - 1$$
$$= 5(5^k - 1) + 4.$$

The aim of this rearrangement is to be able to utilise the assumption that 4 divides $f(k) = 5^k - 1$. Under this assumption it is clear that $5(5^k - 1) + 4$, and hence $f(k+1)$, is divisible by 4. Thus we have shown that $f(k)$ being divisible by 4 implies that $f(k+1)$ is also divisible by 4.

Of course you might feel a little uncomfortable about the inductive hypothesis. How can we just assume that 4 divides $f(k)$ when that is what we are trying to prove in the first place? The answer to this has a beautiful simplicity to it. Since k could be any positive integer, we set $k = 1$. It follows, from the argument in the previous paragraph, that if $f(1)$ is divisible by 4 then $f(2)$ is also divisible by 4. However, it has already been shown that 4 does divide $f(1)$, so $f(2)$ is indeed divisible by 4. Next we set $k = 2$. Since 4 divides $f(2)$ it follows that 4 also divides $f(3)$.

You can probably now see that we have set an unstoppable chain of implications in motion. This process can continue indefinitely, thereby proving that $f(n)$ is divisible by 4 for all positive integers n.

Notice that there were two essential elements to the proof:

(i) Showing that the truth of the statement for $n = k$ implies the truth of the statement for $n = k + 1$.

(ii) Showing that the statement is actually true for some value of n (in this case $n = 1$). This part of the proof is called the *initialisation*, and it validates the infinite sequence of implications.

Let us look at one more example. We will prove the following result concerning the sum of the first n squares

$$1^2 + 2^2 + 3^2 + \cdots + n^2 = \frac{n(n+1)(2n+1)}{6}.$$

Initialisation   Since

$$\frac{1 \times (1+1)(2 \times 1 + 1)}{6} = \frac{1 \times 2 \times 3}{6} = 1 = 1^2$$

the statement is true for $n = 1$.

Inductive hypothesis   Let us suppose that the statement is true for some $n = k$. Then

$$1^2 + 2^2 + 3^2 + \cdots + k^2 + (k+1)^2 = \left[1^2 + 2^2 + 3^2 + \cdots + k^2\right] + (k+1)^2$$

$$= \frac{k(k+1)(2k+1)}{6} + (k+1)^2$$

on using the inductive hypothesis. However,

$$\frac{k(k+1)(2k+1)}{6} + (k+1)^2 = \frac{k+1}{6}[k(2k+1) + 6(k+1)]$$

$$= \frac{k+1}{6}\left(2k^2 + 7k + 6\right)$$

$$= \frac{(k+1)(k+2)(2k+3)}{6}$$

$$= \frac{(k+1)[(k+1)+1][2(k+1)+1]}{6}$$

from which we see that that the truth of the statement for $n = k$ implies the truth of the statement for $n = k + 1$, thereby completing the proof by the principle of mathematical induction.

Appendix B

The generalised binomial theorem

In Chapter 1 it was shown that for any positive integer n, the coefficient of x^k in $(1+x)^n$ is given by

$$\binom{n}{k} = \frac{n(n-1)(n-2)\ldots(n-k+1)}{k!}.$$

The expression on the right is actually defined for any real number n and positive integer k, and this can be used to generalise the binomial theorem to all real n. There is, however, one major difference between the expansions that arise when n is a positive integer and those that arise when n is not. If n is a positive integer then

$$\frac{n(n-1)(n-2)\ldots(n-k+1)}{k!} = 0$$

for all integers $k \geq n+1$ so we end up with a finite series. On the other hand, when n is not a positive integer it is clear that this expression can never be zero. In this case an infinite series will result. This makes life a little bit more complicated since we will now need to consider the values of x for which the series converges.

Here are two examples to illustrate the generalised binomial theorem.

First, let us expand $\sqrt{1+x}$:

$$\sqrt{1+x} = 1 + \frac{\left(\frac{1}{2}\right)}{1!}x + \frac{\left(\frac{1}{2}\right)\left(\frac{1}{2}-1\right)}{2!}x^2 + \frac{\left(\frac{1}{2}\right)\left(\frac{1}{2}-1\right)\left(\frac{1}{2}-2\right)}{3!}x^3$$
$$+ \frac{\left(\frac{1}{2}\right)\left(\frac{1}{2}-1\right)\left(\frac{1}{2}-2\right)\left(\frac{1}{2}-3\right)}{4!}x^4 + \cdots$$

$$= 1 + \frac{\left(\frac{1}{2}\right)}{1!}x + \frac{\left(\frac{1}{2}\right)\left(-\frac{1}{2}\right)}{2!}x^2 + \frac{\left(\frac{1}{2}\right)\left(-\frac{1}{2}\right)\left(-\frac{3}{2}\right)}{3!}x^3$$
$$+ \frac{\left(\frac{1}{2}\right)\left(-\frac{1}{2}\right)\left(-\frac{3}{2}\right)\left(-\frac{5}{2}\right)}{4!}x^4 + \cdots$$

$$= 1 + \tfrac{1}{2}x - \tfrac{1}{8}x^2 + \tfrac{1}{16}x^3 - \tfrac{5}{128}x^4 + \cdots .$$

You will spot straight away that this expansion is certainly not valid for all x. In fact, this series only converges when $-1 \le x \le 1$.

When x is small it is possible to obtain some very accurate approximations using just the first 3 or 4 terms of the series. Let us, for example, use the above series to obtain an approximation for $\sqrt{1.01}$. On setting $x = 0.01$ we obtain

$$\sqrt{1.01} \approx 1 + \tfrac{1}{2}(0.01) - \tfrac{1}{8}(0.01)^2 + \tfrac{1}{16}(0.01)^3 = 1.0049875625.$$

This is actually correct to 10 significant figures.

As a second example:

$$\frac{1}{(1-3x)^2} = 1 + \frac{(-2)}{1!}(-3x) + \frac{(-2)(-2-1)}{2!}(-3x)^2$$
$$+ \frac{(-2)(-2-1)(-2-2)}{3!}(-3x)^3 + \cdots$$

$$= 1 + \frac{(-2)}{1!}(-3x) + \frac{(-2)(-3)}{2!}(9x^2)$$
$$+ \frac{(-2)(-3)(-4)}{3!}(-27x^3) + \cdots$$

$$= 1 + 6x + 27x^2 + 108x^3 + \cdots .$$

This expansion is valid for $-\frac{1}{3} < x < \frac{1}{3}$.

The binomial theorem has a long historical pedigree, and was considered in turn by the trio of mathematical greats Isaac Newton, Leonhard

Euler and Carl Friedrich Gauss (in the 17th, 18th and 19th centuries respectively). Prior to the 19th century the necessity for mathematically rigorous proofs was not yet fully realised, and indeed neither Newton nor Euler gave proofs of the binomial theorem that would be regarded today as totally rigorous. Gauss gave the first real proof of the generalised binomial theorem in 1812, and in fact Gauss's work represented the first time that *anything* about infinite sums was proved in a totally satisfactory fashion.

Appendix C

Expressing integers in non-decimal bases

The decimal system is based on the number 10, which we call the *base*. Ten digits are required to write down numbers in decimal, 0, 1, 2, ..., 9. We also need to know that the place value is based on powers of 10. For example, 30 928 in decimal can be expressed in the form

$$30\,000 + 900 + 20 + 8 = 3 \times 10^4 + 0 \times 10^3 + 9 \times 10^2 + 2 \times 10^1 + 8 \times 10^0.$$

However, there is nothing particularly special about the number 10, other than the fact that this is the number of fingers and thumbs possessed by humans (we undoubtedly used our fingers and thumbs to help us when the concept of counting was first introduced), and it is just as easy to devise a number system using a different base.

The *binary* number system is, because of its association with the workings of computers, a well-known alternative to the decimal system. It is based on the number 2 and is in some sense the most efficient number system in that it only requires two digits, 0 and 1. We do, however, pay for this simplicity somewhat because the binary representation of an integer larger than 1 will be longer than the decimal representation of the same integer. The binary number 11010, for example, represents

$$1 \times 2^4 + 1 \times 2^3 + 0 \times 2^2 + 1 \times 2^1 + 0 \times 2^0 = 16 + 8 + 2 = 26$$

in decimal.

It is extremely simple to convert decimal numbers to binary. Let us demonstrate this procedure with the number 43. Start by finding the largest power of 2 not exceeding 43, which is $2^5 = 32$. Then subtract this from 43 to give 11. Next, find the largest power of two not exceeding 11 and subtract this from 11. This continues until we end up with zero, to give us

$$43 = 2^5 + 2^3 + 2^1 + 2^0$$
$$= 1 \times 2^5 + 0 \times 2^4 + 1 \times 2^3 + 0 \times 2^2 + 1 \times 2^1 + 1 \times 2^0.$$

From this it can be seen that 101011 is the binary representation of 43.

A key fact is that any given positive integer has a unique representation base n for each integer $n \geq 2$. In order to write down numbers using base n we require n distinct digits. When $n = 3$ we have the *ternary* number system, which uses the digits 0, 1 and 2. You might like to check that the decimal number 195 is 21020 in ternary.

Appendix D

One-to-one correspondence

We first consider one-to-one correspondences between finite sets, starting with a particularly simple example. Let S and T be the sets of integers given by

$$S = \{1, 2, 3, 4, \ldots, 286, 287\} \text{ and } T = \{25, 32, 39, 46, \ldots, 2\,020, 2\,027\}.$$

Note that there is the following relationship between the elements in S and T:

$$7 \times 1 + 18 = 25,$$
$$7 \times 2 + 18 = 32,$$
$$7 \times 3 + 18 = 39,$$
$$\vdots$$
$$7 \times 287 + 18 = 2\,027.$$

This relationship may be regarded as a *mapping* (function) from S to T. In other words, there is some rule that gets us from elements in S to elements in T (in this case the rule is 'multiply by 7 and then add 18'). It is important to notice that under this mapping every element of S gets mapped to some element of T, no two distinct elements of S get mapped to the same element of T and every element of T gets mapped to by some element of S. A mapping with these properties provides us with a one-to-one correspondence between the elements in S and those in T.

In summary, a one-to-one correspondence (also termed a *bijective mapping*) between two finite sets S and T can be thought of as a mapping from S to T with the following key properties:

(a) No two distinct elements of S get mapped to the same element of T. Such a mapping is termed *one-to-one*.

(b) For any given element x of T there exists some element in S that gets mapped to x. A mapping of this type is called *onto*.

The fact that a one-to-one correspondence has been established between the elements in the finite set S and those in the finite set T means that the number of elements in both sets is the same. Thus, since there are clearly 287 elements in S, there must also be 287 elements in T. We have therefore found the number of elements in T without counting them explicitly. Of course, in this simple example it would have been quicker just to perform the calculation

$$1 + \frac{2\,027 - 25}{7} = 287.$$

However, in many situations in mathematics counting the number of elements in a set can be a very difficult problem indeed. For example, the set might contain unwieldy combinatorial objects (as is the case for many of the problems considered in this book). In these circumstances we might look to establish a one-to-one correspondence between the elements in this set and the elements in a set that we already know something about. If there were a formula available for the number of elements in the latter set then this would automatically serve as a formula for the number of elements in the former set.

It is also possible to establish a one-to-one correspondence between two infinite sets. For example, let A be the set of all positive integers and E be the set of all positive even integers. Let us consider the mapping from A to E given by 'multiply by 2'. Note that the key properties (a) and (b) given above are certainly satisfied so there is indeed a one-to-one correspondence between the positive integers and the positive even integers. Of course the issue of the 'size' of these sets requires a lot more thought than was the case for finite sets. May we interpret this one-to-one correspondence as saying that these sets have the 'same size' in some sense? This idea might seem rather counter-intuitive, bearing in mind that the positive even integers are a proper subset of the positive integers. This is something for you to consider at some point in your mathematical studies.

Appendix E

Table of central binomial coefficients and Catalan numbers

n	$^{2n}C_n$	C_n
0	1	1
1	2	1
2	6	2
3	20	5
4	70	14
5	252	42
6	924	132
7	3 432	429
8	12 870	1430
9	48 620	4 862
10	184 756	16 796
11	705 432	58 786
12	2 704 156	208 012
13	10 400 600	742 900
14	40 116 600	2 674 440
15	155 117 520	9 694 845

Hints to the Challenges

Chapter 1

Challenge 1.1

A scientific calculator would certainly come in handy for this Challenge. The total time required is $27! \times 30$ seconds. To get the answer you can work out the number of seconds there are in 13 billion years and then perform a division.

Challenge 1.2

When trying to prove a general result such as this it is often a good idea to try out some numerical examples first in order to get a feel for the problem. You will see that a certain amount of cancelling occurs to give

$$\frac{m!}{k!(m-k)!} = \frac{m(m-1)(m-2)\dots(m-k+1)}{k!}$$

(indeed, looking ahead, you will notice that this appears as (1.2) in this chapter). The numerator on the right is the product of k consecutive positive integers so you will have completed the Challenge if you can show that $k!$ always divides such an expression.

As a final hint, note that the product of k consecutive positive integers is certainly divisible by any integer m with $1 \le m \le k$. This is not quite enough to prove what is required, but it should get you started.

Challenge 1.3

Just as we can use Pascal's triangle to obtain the coefficients for the binomial expansion $(1+x)^n$, we can use Pascal's pyramid to get the coefficients for the trinomial expansion $(1 + x + y)^n$, as referred to in the statement of this challenge. For further information about Pascal's pyramid visit the website [17].

Challenge 1.4

Use the recurrence relation (1.3) to express $^{2n}C_n$ as the sum of two binomial coefficients that are, by the symmetry property (1.1), equal.

Chapter 2

Challenge 2.1

Construct a similar argument to the one we used to prove Result 2.6(b).

Chapter 4

Challenge 4.1

You only need to consider the exponents of two of the primes in the prime factorisation of $1\,000!$, one of which will give you the number of zeros.

Challenge 4.2

Let us suppose that n is written in base p. Then the number comprising of the k rightmost digits of n is given by

$$n - p^k \left\lfloor \frac{n}{p^k} \right\rfloor.$$

There will be a carry when n is added to itself in base p whenever

$$2\left(n - p^k \left\lfloor \frac{n}{p^k} \right\rfloor\right) \geq p^k, \ k = 1, 2, 3, \dots.$$

Now see if you can rearrange this inequality in such a way as to relate it to the ideas used to prove Result 4.2.

Chapter 5

Challenge 5.1

Try making the substitution $x = \cot u$ in the improper integral.

Challenge 5.2

Set $n = 10^m$ in Result 5.3 and take logarithms base 10.

Chapter 7

Challenge 7.1

You just need to show that $\dfrac{C_n \sqrt{n^3 \pi}}{2^{2n}} \to 1$ as $n \to \infty$.

Chapter 8

Challenge 8.1

This can be done starting with the results

$$\sum_{k=0}^{m} \frac{1}{2^k} \binom{k+m}{m} = 2^m \quad \text{and} \quad \sum_{k=0}^{\infty} \frac{1}{2^k} \binom{k+m}{m} = 2^{m+1},$$

both of which you might want to prove first.

Challenge 8.2

Consider the total number of possible outcomes for a sequence consisting of n red and n blue balls, and then figure out the number of those outcomes that will ensure you never step over the edge of the pool.

Chapter 9

Challenge 9.1

This can be done by comparing the coefficient of x^{n-1} on both sides of

$$[G(x)]^2 \equiv \frac{1}{1 - 4x},$$

an identity which follows from (6.2). Remember that $G(x)$ is the generating function for the central binomial coefficients.

Chapter 10

Challenge 10.1

Consider the integral defined by

$$I_k = \int_0^1 x^{2n-k}(1-x)^k \, dx$$

and establish a reduction formula. The integral I_0 is easy to evaluate and we then need an expression for I_n.

Challenge 10.2

This is a reasonably demanding Challenge. I obtained this result by considering the sum of a series whose nth term is $2^n B(n,n)$, where $B(k,m)$ is the *beta function*, a function that is mentioned in Chapter 10. The beta function is generally defined via an integral but when n is a positive integer $B(n,n)$ is 'almost' the reciprocal of $2^{(n-1)}C_{n-1}$.

Chapter 11

Challenge 11.1

One way of doing this is by showing that the number of distinct binary trees on n nodes satisfies the Catalan recurrence relation (7.1). Consider the subtrees on either side of the root. You could have a subtree consisting of $n-1$ nodes on the left of the root and nothing on the right of it, or you could have a subtree consisting of $n-2$ nodes on the left of the root and a subtree consisting of just 1 node on the right of it, and so on. You may find it helpful to draw some examples in order to see exactly what is going on.

Challenge 11.2

Look at the entries in the middle of the even-numbered rows of Pascal's triangle and the entries next to these. In order to prove your conjecture, write down, in terms of binomial coefficients, the difference between these entries for the $(2n)$th row. A little bit of algebraic manipulation should then do the trick.

Challenge 11.3

Let H_n be the number of possible arrangements of handshakes for $2n$ people. First explain why, for example, person 1 cannot shake hands with an odd-numbered person. Then show that H_n obeys the Catalan recurrence relation by considering in turn all possible arrangements in which 1 shakes hands with 2, all possible arrangements in which 1 shakes hands with 4, all possible arrangements in which 1 shakes hands with 6, and so on. For example, when 1 shakes hands with 8 the table is effectively split up into two smaller tables consisting of 6 people and $2(n-4)$ people, respectively. All you need do then is to ensure that the initial conditions of the recurrence relation for H_n match those for the Catalan recurrence relation.

Challenge 11.4

The suggested one-to-one correspondence is possibly a little more difficult to establish than some of the others we have looked at. There are n triangles and n nodes so you might be able to match these up in some way. In particular, you will need to think about which of the n triangles you are going to assign to the root each time. You can assign arcs between nodes if the triangles representing them have an edge in common.

Chapter 12

Challenge 12.1

It is straightforward, using the Catalan recurrence relation, to show that C_n is even when n is even. When n is odd but not equal to $2^k - 1$ for some k then you can adapt the inductive argument given to show that C_n will be even.

Chapter 13

Challenge 13.1

Use a similar method to the one we used to obtain (13.6) from (13.4).

Challenge 13.2

Note that 1 is not a prime and that 2 is the only even prime, and then think carefully about what $\pi(2^{k+1})$ is enumerating.

Answers and hints to the Exercises

Exercise 1

1. (a) 35   (b) 120   (c) 190.

2. (a) $^{14}C_7 = 3432$
    (b) $(-1)^7 \times {}^{14}C_7 = -3432$
    (c) $2^7 \times {}^{14}C_7 = 439\,296$.

3. For the combinatorial proof, consider a squad of n players. If you want to choose a team of m players from this squad such that one member of the team is captain, then there are

$$m\binom{n}{m}$$

ways of doing this. This is the left-hand side. Now try to enumerate the same thing in a way that will give the right-hand side.

For the algebraic derivation of this result you can use (1.2).

4. This might look a little daunting at first, but in order to prove (a) and (b) simply insert appropriate values of x in (1.4). To obtain result (c) you can start by differentiating both sides of (1.4) with respect to x.

5. (b) A generalisation of the results from part (a) is given by

$$\binom{n}{m}\binom{m}{k} = \binom{n}{k}\binom{n-k}{m-k},$$

where $n \geq m \geq k \geq 0$. In order to prove the above result it is simply a matter of manipulating the factorials.

6. This is the hardest question in this exercise. Start by proving that

$$F_{n+1} = \sum_{k=0}^{m} \binom{n-k}{k},$$

where $m = \frac{n}{2}$ if n is even and $m = \frac{n-1}{2}$ if n is odd. This can be done by induction, using (1.3). Then note that the result you have been asked to prove is a special case of the above.

Exercise 2

1. 29, 31, 37, 41, 43 will definitely divide $^{46}C_{23}$ while 17, 19 and 23 will not.

2. Result 2.6 shows, for example, that 37 divides $^{50}C_{25}$ but does not divide $^{76}C_{38}$.

3. At the end of Chapter 1 we made an observation that is equivalent to the fact that $^{2n}C_n$ enumerates the number of arrangements of n indistinguishable boys and n indistinguishable girls in a line. Note that there are exactly $^{2n-1}C_{n-1}$ arrangements such that a boy is at position $2n$, there are exactly $^{2n-2}C_{n-1}$ arrangements such that a girl is at position $2n$ and a boy is at position $2n - 1$, there are exactly $^{2n-3}C_{n-1}$ arrangements such that both position $2n - 1$ and position $2n$ are occupied by girls while position $2n - 2$ is occupied by a boy, and so on. This hint, together with (1.1), should be enough for you to complete the proof.

4. If you get really stuck on this then look ahead to the working at the end of the proof of Result 5.1 on page 39.

5. The right-hand side inequality can be proved by noting that

$$2^{2n+1} = (1+1)^{2n+1}$$
$$= \binom{2n+1}{0} + \binom{2n+1}{1} + \cdots$$
$$+ \binom{2n+1}{n} + \binom{2n+1}{n+1} + \cdots + \binom{2n+1}{2n+1}$$
$$> \binom{2n+1}{n} + \binom{2n+1}{n+1}$$

for $n \geq 1$. Now see if you can adapt the second half of the proof of Result 2.5 to obtain the given lower bound.

6. As in the hint to question 4 above, imagine n indistinguishable boys and n indistinguishable girls standing in a line. In order to prove the given result, we can draw an imaginary line between the $(n-1)$th and the nth person. To the left of this line (that is, amongst the first $n-1$ students) it is possible that there might be no girls at all. If this is the case then there must be n girls to the right of the line. If there is exactly 1 girl to the left of the line then there must be $n-1$ girls to the right of it, and so on. Finally, to obtain the stated result, just use (1.1).

Exercise 3

1. (a) $^{18}C_9 = 48\,620$ (b) $^{24}C_{12} = 2\,704\,156$.

2. $^{10}C_5 = 252$.

3. $^{50}C_{25} \approx 1.26 \times 10^{14}$.

4. $\dfrac{^8C_4}{6^5} = \dfrac{35}{3\,888}$.

5. (a) Draw a 7×7 grid such that one corner has coordinates $(0,0)$ and the opposite corner is at $(7,7)$. On forming a path from $(0,0)$ to $(7,7)$ note that it must pass through either $(0,3)$, $(1,2)$, $(2,1)$ or $(3,0)$.

   (b) A generalisation of this result is

$$\binom{3}{0}\binom{2n-3}{n} + \binom{3}{1}\binom{2n-3}{n-1}$$
$$+ \binom{3}{2}\binom{2n-3}{n-2} + \binom{3}{3}\binom{2n-3}{n-3} = \binom{2n}{n},$$

   but note that this can itself be generalised.

Exercise 4

1. (a) 3   (b) 4   (c) 1   (d) $\frac{25}{24}$.

2. (a) $2^3 \times 3 \times 7^3 \times 23$

(b) $2^{26} \times 3^{14} \times 5^7 \times 7^4 \times 11^2 \times 13^2 \times 17 \times 19 \times 23 \times 29 \times 31$

(c) $2^2 \times 3^2 \times 5 \times 7 \times 11 \times 13 \times 23 \times 29 \times 31 \times 37$.

3. (a) $f(2) = 3$, $f(3) = 2$, $f(5) = 1$, $f(7) = 1$ and $f(11) = 1$.

4. If you find that you are not getting anywhere with this problem then calculate the expression for various integer values of k and m in order to see what is going on. Once you are reasonably sure you have the answer then you should try to prove it.

5. $\frac{1}{4}(5^k - 1)$.

6. (a) 4   (b) 4   (c) 8   (d) 1.

7. (a) $\dfrac{2^n C_n}{2^{2n}}$ (b) $\dfrac{2^n C_n \times 9^n}{10^{2n}}$.

Exercise 5

1. (a) (i) 258
       (ii) 187 079
       (iii) 138 710 677 319.
   (b) (i) 6 and 2.4%
       (ii) 2 323 and 1.3%
       (iii) 864 148 500 and 0.63%.

2. $((3!)!)!$ $\sqrt{\binom{400}{200}}$ $\binom{200}{100}$ $\binom{100}{50}^2$ $46!$.

3. You can use Result 5.3 to give

$$\binom{2n}{n} + \binom{2(n+1)}{n+1} \sim \frac{2^{2n}}{\sqrt{n\pi}} + \frac{2^{2(n+1)}}{\sqrt{(n+1)\pi}}$$
$$= \frac{2^{2n}}{\sqrt{\pi}}\left[\frac{1}{\sqrt{n}} + \frac{2^2}{\sqrt{n+1}}\right].$$

This just now needs some careful manipulation to achieve the required result.

4. Use (1.5) in conjunction with Result 5.4 (Stirling's formula).

5. Employ a similar method to the one used to obtain an asymptotic relation for $F(n) = 1 + 2 + 3 + \cdots + n$ earlier in the chapter.

6. (b) You may assume the result $\left(1+\frac{1}{n}\right)^n \to e$ as $n \to \infty$.

7. π.

8. (b) Make repeated use of the result from part (a) and then employ the result from question 4 in Exercise 2.

Exercise 6

1. (a) $\frac{1}{\sqrt{5}}$ (b) $\frac{3\sqrt{3}}{4}$ (c) $\frac{1}{\sqrt{2}}$.

2. (a) $48\sqrt{2}$ (b) $\frac{5\sqrt{2}-1}{4}$.

3. Obtain this result by generalising the method you used to get the answer to 2(a).

4. $\frac{1}{6}\left(3 - \sqrt{5}\right)$.

Exercise 7

1. We know that $2^{(n+1)}C_{n+1}$ is an integer. Thus, from (1.6),

$$\frac{2(2n+1)}{n+1}\binom{2n}{n}$$

is an integer. Now construct an argument to show that this implies that $2^n C_n$ is divisible by $n+1$ for all non-negative integers n.

2. (b) $C_6 = 132$, $C_7 = 429$ and $C_8 = 1430$.

3. Since $C_{91} \approx 4 \times 10^{51}$ the number of sides of the polygon is 93.

4. This problem is considered in greater depth in chapter 12.

5. Consider an allowed voting pattern on $2n$ votes. If candidate a did not receive the first two votes then the first two votes cast must have been AB. If we remove these votes from the allowed voting pattern then what remains is an allowed voting pattern on $2(n-1)$ votes. Furthermore, any allowed voting pattern on $2(n-1)$ votes will, by appending AB to the front of it, give rise to an allowed voting pattern on $2n$ votes. This should be more than enough to get you started!

Exercise 8

1. (a) $\dfrac{^{10}C_5}{2^{10}} = \dfrac{63}{256}$ (b) $\dfrac{^{10}C_5}{2^{10}(2 \times 5 - 1)} = \dfrac{7}{256}$.

2. $2\,001\,130$.

3. (a) $\dfrac{^{2n}C_n \times 5^n}{6^{2n}}$ (b) 20.

4. $\dfrac{1}{6}\left[\dfrac{^2C_1}{2^2} + \dfrac{^4C_2}{2^4} + \dfrac{^6C_3}{2^6} + \dfrac{^8C_4}{2^8} + \dfrac{^{10}C_5}{2^{10}} + \dfrac{^{12}C_6}{2^{12}}\right] = \dfrac{1\,979}{6\,144}$.

5. In generalising the situation from question 4, we end up with the sum

$$\frac{1}{n}\sum_{k=1}^{n}\frac{^{2n}C_n}{2^{2n}}.$$

Now use induction to show that

$$\sum_{k=1}^{n}\frac{^{2n}C_n}{2^{2n}} = \frac{2n+1}{2^{2n}}\binom{2n}{n} - 1 \text{ for all } n \geq 1.$$

6. A proof of this result is given in [6].

Exercise 9

1. (a) By comparing the coefficient of x^k on both sides of the identity, we obtain the general result

$$\sum_{j=0}^{k}\binom{m}{j}\binom{n}{k-j} = \binom{m+n}{k},$$

noting that ^nC_r is defined to be zero when $r > n$.

(b) $\dbinom{26}{11} = 7\,726\,160$.

2. Suppose that a school has m male and n female teachers. A committee consisting of k of the teachers is to be formed in order to organise the staff Christmas party. Count the number of possible committees in two different ways.

3. Hopefully the identity to be used to obtain the given result is fairly obvious. You just need to be careful to interpret the sum on the left-hand side correctly.

4. (a) On expanding both brackets on the left-hand side you will find that all the odd powers of x cancel out.

5. Adapt the method outlined in question 4. The expression will look very similar to the one obtained in 4(c).

Exercise 10

1. You will find that the integral given in (10.1) is undefined when t is a negative integer.

2. $\frac{15\sqrt{\pi}}{8}$.

3. (a) $\frac{4}{\pi}$.

   (b) This formula can be obtained by using the results $\Gamma\left(\frac{1}{2}\right) = \sqrt{\pi}$, $\Gamma(t) = (t-1)\Gamma(t-1)$ and $^{2t}C_t = \Gamma(2t+1) \div [\Gamma(t+1)]^2$, all given earlier in the chapter.

4. If you expand the integrand and then evaluate the integral you will obtain the sum on the left-hand side. To show that this integral also evaluates to the right-hand side you might find that your research into the beta function comes in handy.

Exercise 13

1. (a) 9   (b) 3   (c) 25.

2. $3 \leq \pi(100) \leq 130$ and $9\,048 \leq \pi(1\,000\,000) \leq 434\,294$.

3. (b) $162\,756$.

4. Approximately $60\,000$ primes.

5. $m = 9$ and $n = 10$ or $m = n = 10$.

6. See [1], for example.

Exercise 15

1. The proof of Result 15.2 can be adapted quite easily. Instead of considering $f(p)$ and $f(-2p)$, consider $f((n-1)p)$ and $f(-np)$.

2. Let p be any prime. We already know that each of the coefficients $a_1, a_2, \ldots, a_{p-2}$ of the polynomial

$$f(x) = x^{p-1} + a_{p-2}x^{p-2} + \cdots + a_1 x + a_0$$

is divisible by p, and also that $a_0 = f(0) = (p-1)!$. Therefore

$$f(1) = 1 + a_{p-2} + \cdots + a_1 + a_0 = 1 + kp + (p-1)!,$$

for some integer k. However, it is also true that

$$f(1) = (1+1)(1+2)(1+3)\ldots(1+p-1) = p!,$$

showing that $f(1)$ is a multiple of p. This is enough to prove Wilson's theorem.

3. (a) Remembering that p is assumed not to be a factor of n, we see that one of the $p-1$ terms in the product

$$f(n) = (n+1)(n+2)(n+3)\ldots(n+p-1)$$

has to be divisible by p. Then, since

$$f(n) = n^{p-1} + a_{p-2}n^{p-2} + \cdots + a_1 n + a_0$$
$$= n^{p-1} + pk + (p-1)!$$

for some integer k, it follows that p divides $n^{p-1} + (p-1)!$. But from question 2 we know that $(p-1)! \equiv -1 \pmod{p}$. The result follows.

(b) This is just a straightforward application of the result obtained in part (a).

4. 2.

5. 32.

6. From Fermat's little theorem we know that $12^6 \equiv 1 \pmod{7}$. Use this result in conjunction with the fact that $12^3 = 7 \times 247 - 1$ to show what is required.

7. (a) 1

    (b) $(p-2)! \equiv 1 \pmod{p}$ when p is prime.

8. This can be proved by contradiction. Suppose that there exists a composite integer k such that $(k-1)! \equiv -1 \pmod{k}$. Then k possesses some factor m such that $1 < m < k$. This means that m certainly divides $(k-1)!$. Now see if you can obtain the contradiction that will complete the proof.

Bibliography

[1] David M Burton. *Elementary Number Theory*. McGraw-Hill, 1998.

[2] Peter J Cameron. *Combinatorics: Topics, Techniques and Algorithms*. Cambridge University Press, 1994.

[3] J M Child. Theorems on factorials and homogeneous products derived from a theorem of Lagrange. *Mathematical Gazette*, Vol 12 (No 171): pages 158–160, March 1924.

[4] Complicite. A disappearing number [online]. 2007. Available from: http://www.complicite.org/productions/detail.html?id=43.

[5] Stan Dolan. *Discrete Mathematics I*. Cambridge University Press, 2000.

[6] Martin Griffiths. How many children? *Mathematical Gazette*, Vol 90 (No 146): pages 146–149, March 2006.

[7] G H Hardy and E M Wright. *An Introduction to the Theory of Numbers*. Oxford University Press, 1979.

[8] Paul Hoffman. *The Man Who Loved Only Numbers*. Fourth Estate, 1998.

[9] Robert Kanigel. *The Man Who Knew Infinity*. Abacus, 1999.

[10] Donald E Knuth. *The Art of Computer Programming*, volume 1. Addison-Wesley, 1968.

[11] Andrew Lobb. Deriving the nth Catalan number. *Mathematical Gazette*, Vol 83 (No 496): pages 109–110, March 1999.

[12] John J O'Connor and Edmund F Robertson. The MacTutor history of mathematics [online]. Available from: http://www-groups.dcs.st-and.ac.uk/~history/.

[13] H E Rose. *A Course in Number Theory*. Oxford University Press, 1994.

[14] N J A Sloane. The on-line encyclopedia of integer sequences [online]. Available from: http://www.research.att.com/~njas/sequences/.

[15] Richard Stanley and Eric W Weisstein. Catalan number. From MathWorld—A Wolfram Web Resource. Available from: http://mathworld.wolfram.com/CatalanNumber.html.

[16] Eric W Weisstein. Wolstenholme's theorem. From MathWorld—A Wolfram Web Resource. Available from: http://mathworld.wolfram.com/WolstenholmesTheorem.html.

[17] Wikipedia contributors. Pascal's pyramid. Wikipedia, The Free Encyclopedia, 2007. Available from: http://en.wikipedia.org/w/index.php?title=Pascal%27s_pyramid&oldid=177010988.

Index